Weathering Life

By
James Spann

Crest Publishers, LLC
P.O. Box 595 •
Chelsea, Alabama 35043

PROLOGUE

Weather is a relentless opponent. It will bruise and batter you but also take you on an unforgettable ride of a lifetime. Wrestling with the many mysteries of the Earth's atmosphere brings a never-ending quest for knowledge, teaches humility, and means every day in the weather office is different.

I fell in love with weather on summer afternoons in the rural Deep South as a young child in the 1960s. The relationship became complex during the constant severe weather days of the 1970s during my "wonder years." But all these years later, the flame has never faded. In fact, it burns stronger than ever.

On some days I am simply trying to determine if the maximum temperature the next day will be 72 or 78 degrees and when the rain will start. But, on occasion, human lives are dependent on the words I use, the images I show, my body language, and my understanding of a complex atmospheric process. You see, a professional meteorologist does indeed have the ability to save lives on those rare days. No, that isn't some goofy television promo for a news team but the truth.

For a meteorologist, or quite frankly for a person in any other career, everything that happens in life, both good and bad, will prepare the person for one or two days when all of those experiences are needed. And, on a more personal level, the person will be defined by how he or she performs on those days. We all have only a few defining moments in our lives. For weather professionals, our defining moments usually involve some type of extreme event, such as a tornado, hurricane, flood, or winter storm.

For over 40 years, I have publically taken on the challenge of predicting the state of the troposphere, which is about 75 percent of the Earth's atmosphere. It is where most weather occurs, and for meteorologists, it can bring great weeping and gnashing of teeth. In the weather forecasting business, the atmosphere always wins. We just try to stay in the game.

We are given the desires of our hearts, I believe, at birth. For some unknown reason, many people are born with a natural fascination with weather. You know them; they are the ones who don't just check the built-in weather app on their phones. They take a deep dive into meteorological discussions on blogs, openly arguing about which computer model is more accurate, the American GFS or the European ECMWF, and stay up all night when severe storms and tornadoes are a threat. They don't stay up because of fear; they have studied the setup for days and can't wait to see what the atmosphere delivers.

We call them weather geeks, dweebs, nerds, and dorks. If you are reading this book, you just might be one. Some of us are lucky enough to follow a path that leads to a career in meteorology. To this day I still can't believe it; I actually get paid to do the things I love.

I am hoping the words of this book will be an encouragement to those who have a love for weather and even have dreams of becoming professional meteorologists. But I totally understand that most of you reading this aren't planning on forecasting weather for a living. The story of my life just might encourage you as well. Like the weather forecasting business, I have dealt with many peaks, valleys, struggles, dead ends, and breakthroughs. On many days, I wanted to walk away and quit it all. But, through those days, I somehow persevered. That is one of the life traits that I wish for you as you learn more about a child intrigued by the weather and how it all turned into a long, marvelous career.

CHAPTER 1
ALABAMA ROOTS

My birth certificate states that I was born in Huntsville, Alabama, on June 6, 1956. I assume this to be true, but I have no recollection of living there. My mom tells me our family moved to nearby Athens, Alabama, when I was a toddler, but my memory just can't serve up any images of living in the Tennessee Valley. Oddly enough, I have no recollection of my life before the first grade. To be honest, I'm not sure if I went to kindergarten. It is as if my brain didn't function until I turned five.

But what a great place to begin the life of a person who would become fascinated with and fall in love with weather. You see, far North Alabama gets it all, from ice storms to tornadoes to floods to heat waves, to severe thunderstorms, to brutal cold snaps.

Me and my mom.

Some have listed Huntsville as the top tornado city in the United States… not that you really want to have that honor bestowed on your community.

My father was in the business of selling lumber, and he made the decision to move back to his home in Butler County, Alabama, when I was five years old to work in management at W.T. Smith Lumber Company in its company town of Chapman. We would live 10 miles up the road in Greenville, the county seat. This is where those first memories of life begin.

A photo of my father as a young man.

Butler County is in the middle of Deep South Alabama, between Montgomery and Mobile. Often, my mind drifts back to those carefree days growing up in Greenville. I attended W.O. Parmer Elementary School, joined the Cub Scouts, and even took piano lessons for a brief time to gain a little culture. We lived in a house I considered to be a mansion (funny how it looks much smaller today), made many friends, and developed a deep South Alabama drawl. It still exists today, but just hidden underneath the non-regional diction all television people try to project.

My mom and dad. Not sure of the date.

When we moved there in the 1960s, Interstate 65 didn't exist; we used U.S. 31 to drive between Greenville and my grandmother's place in Chapman. Granny Spann lived in a house built by the W.T. Smith Lumber Company.

Me and my cousins at Granny Spann's house in South Butler County (Chapman). About 1960.

It was on a dirt road near the mill, and across the street from the railroad track in the company town. I can't count the number of times I put a penny down on that track, just waiting for the magical flat piece of copper that would emerge, and praying that I wouldn't derail the train and kill the engineers.

The long, hot summer days in the Butler County woods were priceless—there were no smartphones or video games to distract us from nature. Just a bunch of knuckleheads having fun in the blistering Southern sun. I would love to walk down that red dirt road by the railroad tracks again, but when I look at the area with Google Maps satellite data, there is hardly any evidence of that road, and certainly no sign that people used to live by the railroad tracks. But, trains still run through there.

W.T. Smith is now Coastal Forest Products. Maybe one day before I die the new owners will let me come and explore the place that gave me so much joy.

Out in those Butler County woods my buddies and I talked about things we didn't understand--cars, girls, and Vietnam. The deep woods were our protection from some turbulent times in the early 1960s in South Alabama.

Even at a young age I knew something was wrong. I was told you could not go in the same swimming pool used by people of color. I couldn't eat lunch with them, go to school with them, or even be seen with them. I saw a news report on TV about "Bloody Sunday," on March 7, 1965, that took place up the road in Selma. It was beyond my comprehension, and nobody talked to the children about it. But again, I knew something just wasn't right.

Older men at my church, many of them deacons, would openly talk horribly about black people, and express fear that one day they might try to enter the church building.

Those men, who usually wore black suits and had an almost permanent scowl on their faces, disturbed me at first. Later I was afraid of them. They were "church leaders" spewing hate at a place where all should be welcome. They hated black people for sure, and it seemed like they hated kids, even white ones like me.

The culture of racism was alive and well in South Alabama in the 1960s; there are few left alive today that experienced it, or saw it like I did.

To this day you will never see me wearing a suit at church; I don't want to be associated with those people in any way.

But allow me to brag on the Greenville, Alabama, of today. One of my good friends from childhood is now the mayor, Dexter McLendon. Even though it is not in my current TV market, I visit occasionally, speaking in schools and seeing old friends. The South Alabama city is growing, racism has all but faded away, and I could not be more proud of my hometown. I spoke a few years ago at the annual Chamber of Commerce banquet, and the packed room consisted of a remarkable diversity of race and ethnicity.

But, back to the 60s.

Despite the social turmoil around us, we were still innocent.

No, there was no XBox or Playstation, but I did have one fancy piece of electronic equipment: a small transistor radio. I can't recall how it came into my possession, but it was life-changing.

Often on those long summer days, I would flip on that little radio, which was mostly locked in on WBAM in Montgomery, a 50,000 watt blowtorch at 740 on the dial. Owned by the Brennan/Benz families, that station "covered Dixie like the dew." I thought the disc jockeys (DJs) were cool, and they played songs like "Green Onions" by Booker T and the MGs, "Surfin' Safari" by the Beach Boys, and "The Loco-Motion" by Little Eva. But, it was a strange mix of music. . .every once in a while, they would spin something like "Old Rivers" by Walter Brennan, which was when I turned it off.

The only other station with a decent signal that we could get on that radio was WGYV in Greenville, but those disc jockeys were mostly into stuff by Henry Mancini and

Mantovani and his orchestra. They were not exactly targeting 6 and 7-year-old boys as their prime demographic.

I loved hearing the DJs on WBAM. I loved those voices in the small box and thought it would be so cool to be one of those voices. I mean, I really wanted to be the voice in the box. I was sure my dream would come true one day, sooner than later.

On the TV side, we were only able to get one channel on a regular basis: WSFA in Montgomery, Channel 12. I didn't have much interest in watching TV. . .seems like every time I drifted by the old black and white set, Porter Wagoner or something similar was on the air. Nothing against Porter Wagoner, but he just wasn't my thing. I do clearly remember one man who came on the news to talk about weather, Ralph Williams. For some strange reason, I found his show interesting. Ralph would draw on his weather maps with this contraption that looked like a glue bottle, and the fronts, highs, and lows would come out white on his maps.

I never dreamed I would be working on the air for WSFA, later in the next decade, in 1978, after my time on radio as the "voice in the box."

I mentioned that I have no idea if I was ever in kindergarten. But, I remember first grade like it was yesterday.

My first-grade teacher at W.O. Parmer Elementary in Greenville was Edna Earle Porterfield. Quite frankly, she scared me to death. In class, we were all called by our last names. I never knew my friends' first names until second grade. She could wear out a kid's backside with a paddle using intensity and follow through that would impress any high school football or baseball coach. I mean that woman had some serious upper body strength for her age.

Ms. Porterfield was somewhat intense, but boy was she a good teacher. I had a rather strange habit of constantly staring out the window during my first grade days, not being a particularly good listener. One day, she had enough of that and called me out into the hall. I honestly thought my life was about to end at the age of six. But what happened next I call the "Miracle of Greenville, Alabama." No paddling, but a book. She gave me a small book about weather, since she thought I might have a connection because I was always looking out the window. She allowed me to read that book in class over the next few days, and I can safely say it started me on a journey that continues today . . . learning about the Earth's atmosphere and how it works. Funny how little things that seem to happen at random times in our lives can shape and determine who we are.

CHAPTER 2
LIFE WILL NEVER BE THE SAME

Most people experience one or two life-changing moments instantly and unexpectedly. They can't see those moments coming, and accordingly they can't prepare for them. They just happen.

One of those for me came while I was in the second grade, when times were really good. One day in the fall of 1963, my father opted out and walked away from his wife and seven-year-old son. It was like being punched in the gut when you aren't ready for it.

Me about 1970.

The easiest thing for my mother would have been to drop me off at the Alabama Baptist Children's Homes in Troy, just east of Greenville. My mom worked in the office at Greenville High School and didn't make very much money, certainly not enough to support a child and maintain a nice house. But she never thought about any other solution other than keeping me, and I am thankful to this day for that. Thank the Lord for a Godly mom dedicated to her child, during good times and bad. My father never paid one cent toward child support and was totally out of the picture. There were times when my mom told me he promised he could come and visit, but he never showed up. Never.

My mom, not really knowing what to do, decided to move back to her hometown on a temporary basis to try to sort it all out and come up with some kind of plan.

My mom grew up in the northern part of the state in another small town, Ashville, in St. Clair County, which is about 40 miles northeast of Birmingham. This meant leaving my home, friends, and school behind but with the promise that we could get back to Greenville. I transferred temporarily to Ashville Elementary School, where I did have a few friends from the times I would visit my grandmother there, but it was still like being a stranger in a strange land. A South Alabama boy had a hard time living in North Alabama culture.

The fall of 1963 was surreal. On Friday, November 22, I was not feeling well, and stayed home from school. I didn't pay much attention to the black and white TV during the middle of the day, but I generally had it turned on anyway. A moment of silence, followed by a slide that said, "CBS News Bulletin" caught my attention, and I listened as it was reported that President Kennedy was struck by an assassin's bullet in Dallas. Within an hour or so, it was reported that the President was dead. Like my father's sudden departure, it made no sense. Not many seven-year-olds really watched TV news back in those days (or today, for that matter), but for some reason I really locked in to the long-form coverage over that following weekend. Watching Jack Ruby gun down Lee Harvey Oswald and then the funeral of President Kennedy on that black and white television occupied my time and my mind. The funeral for the President was on November 25, and Thanksgiving came on Thursday of that week, November 28. I wish I could recall the family discussion with my mom, my grandmother, and others in the family who joined us for the holiday feast; maybe I just blocked it out of my mind.

My mom moved us back to my beloved home of Greenville after I completed second grade in the summer of 1963. It was so good to be back to my home, my school, and my pals. I finished third and fourth grades at W.O. Parmer; during those years I had a constant hope and dream that my father would return and apologize, and life would get back to normal. But that didn't happen, and my mom had to make some changes for us to survive. And, those changes meant leaving Butler County for good in the summer of 1966 for an odd sounding place called Tuscaloosa.

My mom was enrolling in the University of Alabama to complete her degree in education. She would go on, after graduation, to teach high school English for many years. We moved into a very small apartment at the corner of 10th Street (now called Paul Bryant Drive), and 13th Avenue (now Gene Stallings Avenue). This was within walking distance of the campus and just a couple of blocks west of Denny Stadium, where the University of Alabama played football.

Tuscaloosa looked like Manhattan to me. It was huge compared to Greenville. And somewhat scary. I didn't know anyone, had no father and no siblings, and was going to start fifth grade in a school called Verner Elementary, which was right across the street from Denny Stadium. The college had just finished the bowl by building stands in the south end zone by the school. The stadium then seated about 58,000 people as I recall. The Tide played most of their big home games at Birmingham's Legion Field, which was much larger.

I still had my little transistor radio, the one that was locked into WBAM during all those years in Greenville. I was disturbed to find out that WBAM's signal in Tuscaloosa was weak and full of static, so I started roaming the radio dial (yes, there was actually a dial back then), looking for something similar. Just down from WBAM's position at 740 KHz was a station booming in on 690 KHz. I listened long enough to find out the call letters were WVOK and that station was coming out of Birmingham. The station called itself the "mighty 690," and as it turns out it was co-owned with WBAM with some of the same voices and jingles. But, I went up the dial and found one station at 1230 KHz that was loud and strong. The station played really cool music. I learned its call letters were WTBC, and the disc jockeys were the "Good Guys." The one in particular I really liked was Tiger Jack Garrett, who came on in the middle of the day.

I have no idea how many hours I listened to WTBC in the summer of 1966, but listening to it occupied much of my time. The WTBC "Good Guys" were my friends, and started me on the process of warming up to Tuscaloosa. Once again, I had no idea I would be working there, at the Big 1230, only seven years later.

I attended Verner Elementary School for 5th and 6th grades; this was the time in my life when my world was the small apartment, that school, and a church on 10th Street called Calvary Baptist Church.

My mom always got me to church on Sundays, and I am thankful to this day she did. At Calvary, I started taking the words taught more seriously, and I made the decision to become a Christian at the age of 12 in 1968. I was baptized by the pastor, Allan Watson, and my journey of faith started. It was, and still is today, the most important thing in my life. You see, Christianity is not a performance-based religion, an allegiance to some political party, or a license to constantly criticize other sinners. It is a relationship with the One who saved me from my sin. The freedom I feel every minute of every day is what gets me through--especially on the hardest days.

One person who made a big difference in my life was the principal at Verner, Archie Hitson. Mr. Hitson knew my situation and was a great encourager. From time to time he would stop me in the hall and say things like "It's going to be OK". . ."You look good today". . .and "I believe in you." I took him at his word and those positive thoughts came at a critical time.

I sold football programs outside Denny Stadium on Saturdays in the fall. If I sold all my programs, I got in the game free at halftime. This was a deal of a lifetime, and I was a good salesman--I got in the games every time.

Sometimes in the spring, I would slip into Foster Auditorium to watch Alabama basketball games. I was there the night Mike Nordholtz put up 50 points against Southern Mississippi in 1967, and that was without the three-point shot. That still stands today as the scoring record in a game for one player.

After Verner Elementary, it was on to Eastwood Junior High School for grades 7, 8, and 9. I wasn't much of an athlete, so I joined the band. Despite very little musical talent, I played French horn, a rather difficult instrument to play. Guys in the brass section sure weren't chick magnets like the guys in the drum line. But, I enjoyed being in the band; it was a great way of learning teamwork.

The first band trip I recall was to the new "Six Flags Over Georgia" when I was in the 8th grade in the spring of 1970. I think every boy in the band bought a whoopee cushion at Six Flags, making the bus ride home pretty miserable. The flatulence noises were funny for maybe two or three minutes, but after that they got old pretty quick. Imagine being on a bus full of middle school boys with "fart bags."

My mom finished her degree and got a job teaching English at Tuscaloosa High School. Soon after that, she was able to move us into a small home on Fairway Drive in Tuscaloosa, which was an amazingly good environment for us. We were in a nice neighborhood, had more room, and had a feeling of "normalcy" for our little family of two.

We did spend time at my grandmother's home in Ashville, mainly during the summers. During the summer of 1969, we were there in mid-August, as Hurricane Camille made the approach to the Gulf Coast. Remember, there were no 24-hour news channels in 1969, but I did have my trusty transistor radio with me. And, as darkness fell on the night of August 16, I tuned into the 50,000-watt blow touch, clear channel WWL in New Orleans at 870 kHz. Those announcers gave pretty much wall-to-wall with coverage of the approaching hurricane. A man named Nash Roberts caught my attention. He really seemed to know his stuff and, as it turned out, I would stay up all night in my bed listening to him and the crew on WWL.

I was very tired when the first light of day came on August 17, meaning WWL was soon going to fade away, and I would not be able to listen as the hurricane made landfall. Camille to this day remains the Gulf Coast hurricane of record. . .at the time of landfall. Re-analysis data showed peak winds of 175 mph along the coast of

Mississippi. A devastating storm tide of 24.6 feet occurred at Pass Christian.

During that all-night radio listening session, the voice in the box this time was talking about weather, and it was a professional meteorologist. A little bit of that coverage by Nash Roberts remains in me today.

CHAPTER 3
ON THE AIR

I recall reading a book about ham radio in the summer of 1970 between my 8th and 9th grade years. For some reason that idea was very appealing to me. I was intrigued at the thought of operating a ham radio, having my own transmitter and receiver at home, and having the potential to communicate with other amateur radio operators anywhere in the world while depending on the conditions of the high frequency bands used by hams.

My ham radio room in Tuscaloosa. About 1971.

I decided to study for the novice class license, the entry level ham radio license offered by the Federal Communications Commission (FCC). I took the exam at a local ham radio operator's home; Bud Peirce was his name, and his call sign was W4KIX. Bud lived not far from our Fairway Drive home, and his ham shack was pure magic: racks of equipment with warm, glowing tubes. Bud loved using Morse Code, or CW (continuous wave) as hams call it. Watching him work that key (he used an older mechanical key called a "bug"), communicating with ham radio operators all over the world, was just too cool. I wanted to be able to do things like that.

Thankfully, I passed on the first try. I had to take a rather simple examination on FCC rules and regulations and electronic theory. At that time I also had to prove Morse Code proficiency at 5 words per minute. A week or so later, my official FCC novice class license came in the mail. My call was WN4SVH and thanks to some loaned equipment from Bud, I was on the air. Back in those days, novice class licensees were limited to Morse Code, but using a wire antenna, I was able to strike up short conversations with other hams in faraway places, not only in the U.S., but abroad as well. I would gather QSL cards, small cards from those I worked on the air that had details of the date, time, and length of the conversation. My QSL card collection would grow, and I hung them on the walls in a small room in our home designated as my shack.

I would go on and earn the General, Advanced, and Extra Class ham licenses at one year intervals; I had to appear before an FCC examiner back in those days for those higher class tickets. I took a Greyhound Bus to Birmingham, where the exams were administered in the Federal Building. I was fortunate to pass all three; after the General Class upgrade my call sign was changed to

WB4SVH, and I earned the Extra Class in the fall of 1973, when I was a senior in high school.

I saved up enough money to buy a Heathkit HW-101 transceiver, which was a dream come true. I had to build the radio from a kit, but by golly it worked, and I didn't think life could get much better. I was heavily involved in nightly Morse Code traffic nets that handled public service messages, and I was doing 50 words per minute at my peak.

Hamfests, or gatherings of amateur radio operators, were special times during these years. I would get to meet many of those I communicated with in person; there were forums, contests, flea markets, and new equipment vendors as well. I was able to attend hamfests in both Birmingham and Huntsville, places where I felt accepted and could hang around people who had the same interests that I had. I still love a good hamfest; we joke on the "Rick and Bubba" radio show even today about them being "magical."

This amateur radio hobby would lay down an important foundation for my career; I learned about electronics and communication, and later it would get me in the storm spotting business. Mentors like Dr. Gordon King in Tuscaloosa (W4XI) became father figures in my life, and I will always be thankful for those men and women in ham radio who accepted a shy teenager with little confidence and not much self-esteem.

My call today is WO4W; I changed from WB4SVH when the FCC opened the door for shorter call signs for those who hold the Extra class license. WO4W was randomly assigned to me by the FCC, but my ham radio buddies decided it stood for "Watching Out 4 Weather." Due to my intense schedule, I don't have as much time to get on the air as I like these days, but later in my retirement years I plan to dive back into the hobby of my childhood.

This artwork was done when I was a senior in high school, working for WTBC in Tuscaloosa. It appeared on a WTBC "Top 40" survey that was distributed at music stores.

CHAPTER 4
DIFFERENT KIND OF RADIO

There is no doubt in my mind it was meant for me to grow up in Tuscaloosa as an older child. I would go on to attend Tuscaloosa High School (THS) 1971-1974; this was one of the two large city high schools and was located on 15th Street, not far from the campus of the University of Alabama and a place where my mom had been teaching English.

I kept on playing the French horn in the band, and between my ham radio hobby and the band, I stayed pretty busy. I didn't have good social skills; I never went to a homecoming dance or a prom. But I had my small circle of friends, and life was good.

No doubt my senior year in high school shaped my future in so many ways. In the summer of 1973, right after my junior year ended, a group of boneheads--including me, of course--built a commercial radio station in the projection room high over the school's auditorium, complete with an audio board, turntables, and a microphone. I took an old Knight Kit DX-150 transmitter I owned to the school and modified it so it would send out an AM signal on 1510 kHz. We put a long wire antenna on the roof of the school and nightly I would tune the variable frequency oscillator (VFO) to the signal of WLAC in Nashville, which operated on 1510 kHz and could be heard easily at night in Tuscaloosa.

We told the school administration this was a very low power station that was perfectly legal, and would give students a chance to learn something about the broadcasting business. Unfortunately, that was a slight stretch of the truth. At times, I cranked the power up to over 100 watts, which was extremely illegal, and the station we called Black Bear Radio (BBR) reached almost all the way across the city including the campus of the University of Alabama.

My principal at THS, Doug Killough, was very supportive, and thankfully he never figured out our illegal power operation. There is a classic YouTube video floating around of a story about WBBR that aired on the local TV station, Channel 33. Mr. Killough and I were interviewed, and I sure sounded like a redneck from Butler County. But, it was an encouragement for those who struggle with a deep Southern accent that want to do weather on television.

We played rock and roll music during the school day on WBBR, and the signal was pumped into the student lounge as well. So, days I was a rock and roll DJ at school, and nights I was working the Morse Code traffic nets at home via ham radio. Really geeky stuff for 1973.

The staff of WBBR radio, the station we built and put on the air when I was in high school.

Soon after my senior year started in September 1973, a local commercial radio station, WTBC called the school office, asking if there was a student there who was willing to work really bad hours for minimum wage. The office gave them my name and the next day I was at the 15th Street studio. After briefly speaking with the program director, I was hired on the spot, and my assignment was to load automation tapes for their FM station, WUOA (95.7 MHz), and record some news and weather tapes that would play on the air. I didn't have a resume, and there was no job application to fill out. In fact, I have never had a resume or filled out an application in my life. I have always had this great fear that one day I will have to get a real job.

In 1973 the big deal was AM. All of the kids in the city listened to WTBC, the BIG 1230. I was working in the same building and was so very close to my dream of being a DJ. I would work weekday mornings signing on to WUOA-FM before school, and then on the weekends I would pretty much camp out at the station running the board for Alabama football games and helping to get all of the sports programming on the air.

My job at WTBC/WUOA would mark the beginning of a long broadcasting career that continues today. I have done so many things in my career, but the most magical event came on a cold Sunday night in November 1973, when a dream came true. I was asked to cross the hall and work my first shift on WTBC--the larger-than-life 1230!

Understand, this was the station I discovered seven years ago when we moved to Tuscaloosa. The greatest songs, the best DJs. Every young person in town listened to the BIG 1230, and the idea of me actually going on that station was almost too much to handle. I was a complete ball of nerves when I hit the air on November 11, 1973, at 6:00 p.m.

My first song on the six-hour shift was "Jessica" by the Allman Brothers. It was the long version; I thought it would give me a chance to calm down and settle the nerves. Nothing in my long career can match the pure excitement I experienced that night. I remember every song I played. Playing those 45 RPM records on the Big 1230, knowing my friends were listening, was pegging the cool meter. Best of all, girls called me. Remember, I was quiet, shy, and not very confident. Not only did high school girls call the request line (345-1230) but college girls as well. There were no iPhones or iPods; people called the local radio station and asked for their songs to be played. It was truly a different world.

What an odd mix of music we played in those days. People who happened to be listening to James Spann's first shift on TBC would have heard current hits like. . .

"Until You Come Back to Me" by Aretha Franklin
"Spiders and Snakes" by Jim Stafford
"Goodbye Yellow Brick Road" by Elton John
"She's Gone" by Hall and Oates (we played it long before it was a commercial hit nationally)
"Hello It's Me" by Todd Rundgren
"Show and Tell" by Al Wilson
"Photograph" by Ringo Starr
"Ramblin' Man" by the Allman Brothers
"D'yer Mak'er" by Led Zepplin
"Livin For the City" by Stevie Wonder

I was paid only $1.65 hour, but the truth is that I would have paid them that much, if not more, for the experience. WTBC actually powered down to just 250 watts after dark, and people could barely hear the station north of the Black Warrior River, but it reached everyone important in my life, and I felt like I was on top of the world.
So often in my life I have thought about that night. That little transistor radio I loved when I was a kid was now inside of me as of November 11, 1973. I had become the "voice in the box."

Late on that magical shift, sometime between 11:00 and 12:00 midnight, it dawned on me that I would have to be back at the station at 4:30 a.m. to sign on the FM station for the start of the Monday morning broadcast day, but the lack of sleep really didn't bother me too much. I often tell people I haven't slept much since 1973, and that is a very true statement. That was the beginning of my sleepless life.

The brutal truth is that I was horrible on the air. My Butler County accent was extremely unprofessional, and I was far from being smooth, funny, or entertaining. That makes me even more thankful to station owner, Bert Bank, for the opportunity. Bert was an American hero; he survived the Bataan Death March during World War II in the 1940s. Truthfully, he was a hard man to work for, but every young man needs a little fear in his life, and Bert was yet another man that stepped in as a father figure for me, a fatherless child.

Looking back on that I am also so thankful for my mom; that must have been so bewildering. Ham radio, wires and antennas all over our house, and me working at a commercial radio station at all hours of the day and night. Her giving me the freedom to be me was so important in my life. She gave me nothing but encouragement.

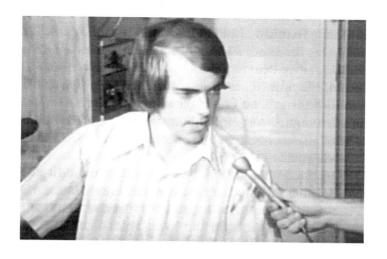

Me being interviewed on WCFT in 1973. Interview was about our high school radio station (this is a screen grab from a YouTube video).

I went through my senior year in high school splitting time between WUOA-FM and the Big 1230, WTBC. But, those AM shifts were my passion and desire. I was willing to work any shift, any time just to get experience. That meant a lot of midnight shifts and weekend shifts. I loved every one of them.

I finally crossed over to the AM side for good late in 1974 when I was a college freshman. On my last morning to read news on WUOA-FM, I played the song "Rock and Roll Hoochie Koo " by Rick Derringer. That decision almost ended my radio job, and most likely any hope of ever doing weather on television.

You see, WUOA played the soft hits. . .songs by artists like Barry Manilow, Jim Croce, and the Carpenters. The format was the syndicated "Hit Parade" by Drake-Chenault, since heavier rock and roll tunes were not allowed. Playing "Rock and Roll Hoochie Koo" during the 7:30-8:00 a.m. half hour meant many were listening while driving to work, including station managers.

An inside source told me there was a fierce debate later that day concerning my future. Some wanted me fired on the spot; others wanted to give me one more chance. I'm not exactly sure who was on my side that day, but that person won the argument, and I was able to keep my job, paving the way for the marvelous career I have enjoyed. I guess sometimes all of us need a little mercy.

CHAPTER 5
THE WEATHER EVENTS THAT STARTED
A CAREER

I have always been interested in weather. Back in
Greenville, I couldn't wait for a good afternoon
thunderstorm on a hot summer day--seeing the towering
clouds, feeling the cool outflow, and hearing the thunder.
But, with the amateur radio license and the ability to drive
when I turned 16, elements were coming together for me
to be a real weather nerd. I often served as net control for
the Tuscaloosa County amateur radio group that also
served as storm spotters during severe weather events. I
spent hours at the Tuscaloosa County Civil Defense
emergency operations center at the Tuscaloosa City Hall.
I should mention that at the time, for some insane reason,
the Emergency Operations Center (EOC) was in the attic
of that building, the worst possible place in the event of a
tornado. A few years later it was thankfully moved to the
basement.

Keep in mind that my tenure in Tuscaloosa was during the
decade of the 1970s, which offered some of the most
extreme weather events on record in the state of Alabama
(and in much of the nation). My first real encounter with
the power of a tornado came on May 27, 1973, right at the
end of my junior year in high school. A strong/violent,
long-track F4 tornado (now considered an EF-4 on the
newer, enhanced Fujita scale) ripped through a number of
Central Alabama communities that evening, and a group
of amateur radio operators from Tuscaloosa was
dispatched to Brent, in Bibb County, about 30 miles to the
southeast down U.S. 82.

Understand that in 1973 there were no cell phones, and amateur radio operators played a crucial role in the communication process during any emergency-- and they still do today. We were one of the first relief crews to arrive, and I will never forget those moments: seeing the total darkness due to the lack of power, the unspeakable damage caused by the tornado, and the real human suffering eye to eye. There was also a very odd odor in Brent; later I would learn from some first responders that it is called the "scent of death." Since, I have noticed this at a number of violent tornado scenes in the hours after the storm passed, and nobody seems to know what it is or why it is there. Part of the odor is from damaged pine trees, but the rest is a nasty sulphur-type smell. It is almost as if it stays on the clothes or body for days.

In all, five people died in Brent, including one man who was attending services at the Brent Baptist Church. Andrew Mitchell died at the church between Training Union, and the Sunday evening worship service. It has been my honor to speak from the pulpit at that church a number of times in the years that have followed.

We returned to Tuscaloosa late that night, but the next morning we were back in Bibb County, establishing a station at the Centreville Baptist Church, where emergency services were being coordinated. I worked at that station for several days, handling a variety of emergencies and health and welfare traffic messages. It was a life-changing experience and planted something in me that is still there today--a touch of combined fear and fascination.

That tornado killed seven people and injured 199 others. A total of 216 buildings were destroyed, 570 buildings were damaged, 97 mobile homes were destroyed, and 45 businesses were damaged or destroyed. More than 12,000 acres of timber were destroyed.

A little less than a year later, during the spring of my senior year in high school, came the largest outbreak of tornadoes on record in the United States at that time. . .the "Superoutbreak" of April 3-4, 1974. As usual, that Wednesday night I was the net control operator on the 146.82 MHz net serving Tuscaloosa County from the attic at City Hall. It was a different kind of night. Tornadoes, most of them very large and very violent, kept coming like bullets out of a gun. The warnings were non-stop, and the tone of the call to action messages was so serious. Later, I learned that many of those warnings were written and issued by my future friend and longtime mentor, J.B. Elliott, who was on duty that night at the National Weather Service in Birmingham.

Thankfully, Tuscaloosa County didn't have much damage that night. But, just to the north the scene was like a war zone. The town of Guin, in Marion County, was almost wiped out by an F5 tornado. Another tornado moved right through the middle of Jasper, and there were urgent requests for help from those two communities and many other locations across North Alabama.

I was dispatched to Jasper that night. After leaving Tuscaloosa, I made the long drive up Alabama Highway 69, and upon entering the Jasper City limits, I was escorted by a police officer to the People's Hospital. I was told to set up my equipment in the emergency room of the hospital, and it was my job to relay requests for supplies and medical resources back to various relief agencies in Birmingham. The 146.94 W4CUE repeater on Shades Mountain in Birmingham was a lifeline that night.

The unforgettable part of the night was seeing the grotesque nature of the wounds being treated in the emergency room. I had always wanted storms and tornadoes to happen so I could be net control and enjoy the adrenaline rush that comes along with working a severe weather event. Being in that old EOC in the Tuscaloosa City Hall attic with the National Weather Service teletype machine was exhilarating. But, that night made me rethink it all. I still loved weather, but I had clear knowledge of the need for doing something to prevent this kind of injury and death. That was a big part of the journey that led to a long career in meteorology. That night gave me night terrors for a few years, and to this day I have never discussed details with anyone, publicly or privately. I guess I just had to experience it for some unknown reason. It was the night I lost my innocence.

I drove back home to Tuscaloosa during the early morning hours April 4. But later I hit the road again heading back into North Alabama as the need was great for amateur radio operators. I wound up in Huntsville, helping the crew with emergency communications. I also had time to file an audio report with WTBC radio in Tuscaloosa by phone from WAAY-TV atop Monte Sano Mountain in Huntsville.

CHAPTER 6
THE WILD WEATHER OF THE 70S WON'T STOP

I graduated from Tuscaloosa High School in May 1974. I was in the National Honor Society and Mu Alpha Theta (a math honor society) and was named one of the outstanding seniors by the teachers. After the graduation service, instead of going to some party like everyone else, I went to work at WTBC, handling the midnight shift. And, I was delighted to be there.

Nobody told me that meteorology was a viable career option during my senior year in high school despite my love and passion for weather. So, in the fall of 1974, I entered the University of Alabama as an electrical engineering major, still working at WTBC, playing rock and roll music, and still extremely active with my amateur radio hobby. I was living at home with few expenses, and the minimum wage I was making at the radio station was plenty for paying college tuition. Those were different times. And good times.

During my college days, the wild weather of the 70s didn't stop. On February 23, 1975, an F4 tornado moved through the southern part of the city of Tuscaloosa while I was on the air that Sunday afternoon. I was working the 12:00 noon to 6:00 p.m. shift, and about 1:15 the Civil Defense alert radio in the WTBC control room sounded, letting us know a tornado warning had been issued for Tuscaloosa County. That was long before storm-based, polygon warnings. I immediately stopped the song playing and read the basics of the tornado warning. There was no way I could handle long form, wall-to-wall coverage since I had no radar and only a few short lines from the original tornado warning. After the warning was put on the air, I played the song "Lightning Strikes" by Lou Christie. Then, right before that three-minute song ended, the power went out at the studio on 15th Street, and we were off the air.

I stepped out into the parking lot, and for the first time I heard the freight train sound, but the tornado just to the east was rain wrapped and not visible, as is the case with so many Alabama tornadoes. I hopped on the 146.82 MHz repeater, which was on emergency power because I knew this was a bad situation based on the initial reports. My first concern was for my mom who was home at our house on Fairway Drive, near the intersection of Hargrove Road and McFarland Boulevard. There was a real chance the house was hit based on the reports I was hearing, and my heart started racing as I drove that way. As I turned onto our street, I felt a sense of great relief because there was no tornado damage, and all was well.

I was assigned that night to the National Guard Armory in Holt, and worked disaster relief for several days, including storm damage survey work. That was the storm that let me know that a tornado CAN happen in my city, not just somewhere else. It was too close for comfort, but gave me another needed experience in preparation for my career.

One person died in that tornado, Thelma Hill, who was working on the second floor of the Scottish Inn Hotel on McFarland Boulevard in Tuscaloosa. I imagine she had no idea a tornado was coming. Another reminder of the work to be done.

I should note that tornado came before the traditional spring season in Alabama (March, April, and May). The takeaway from this event is that a tornado can happen in any month, and to this day I think the tornado potential in our state is underestimated in January and February, the two months between the fall and spring severe weather seasons. To prove my point, an F3 tornado tore through parts of Pell City and Ragland in St. Clair County just one month earlier on January 10, 1975. One person was killed in that one. People can never let their guards down. And, as I learned from Alan Moller, long-time National Weather Service meteorologist and storm chaser, when it comes to thunderstorms. . .expect the unexpected.

It seems like there was almost non-stop extreme weather through the middle 1970s. Later in 1975, Hurricane Eloise was threatening the Central Gulf Coast during the month of September. I drove down with a friend for that one on the morning of September 22; we took amateur radio gear and were going to help provide emergency communications.

Hurricane warning flags were flying from Grand Isle, Louisiana, to Apalachicola, Florida. In Mobile, where the hurricane was expected to come ashore, businesses and homeowners battened down in preparation for the storm. Civil defense officials set up shelters. Dauphin Island was evacuated, and our destination was Bay Minette, in Baldwin County, where we were to meet with other amateur radio operators.

By late afternoon on September 22, preparations were complete from Pensacola to the west. During the afternoon, attention shifted from the hurricane to a second attempt on President Gerald Ford's life outside the St. Francis Hotel in San Francisco. As if to protest her removal from the top story of the day, Hurricane Eloise began turning more to the northeast and continued to intensify. Warnings were frantically shifted eastward during the late evening, but many people from Fort Walton east to Panama City had already turned in for the night, thinking that landfall was going to be much farther to the west.

The shift in the track meant a shift in our assignment. We wound up in Fort Walton Beach, Florida, about 2:00 a.m. on September 23. We were stationed at Choctawhatchee High School, which was being used as an evacuation center. I will never forget those hours; one lady gave birth at the school shortly before landfall, which came about 7:00 that morning. It was the first hurricane I would experience. We drove all the way back to Tuscaloosa later that day with no sleep.

CHAPTER 7
THE SUMMER OF 1976

Some of my friends and I decided in May of 1976 that we would take a week in June and head for Daytona Beach, a well-known destination for college kids on summer break. Most of us were social zeroes, and I guess we had dreams of driving down there and finding some babes along with the surf and sand. I would turn 20 years old on June 6, and it seemed like a fitting trip.

Turned out the boss at WTBC didn't like the idea, and since we were a bit short staffed, my request for a week off was declined. Now understand, working at TBC was my dream job, and I would probably have paid them to work there. But, in an immature fit of rage, I pretty much told them I was going to Daytona Beach no matter what they said. And, basically Bert Bank told me I was welcome to go but not welcome again at his radio station. I was pretty much kicked out the door on 15th Street on the Friday before we would leave. It never really dawned on me that I was giving up my dream job . . . I just wanted to go have fun with my friends.

So, we all piled into a car and made the long drive south that June, the day after leaving the WTBC studio possibly for the last time. I must admit we had a blast while we were in Daytona Beach. No, we didn't attract any babes, but the weather was great, the water was warm, and the place was packed with interesting people.

One night, two members of our crew found some kind of honky-tonk with mixed drinks for fifty cents. Most of us weren't big drinkers, and we passed up on the opportunity, thankfully. Late that night, those guys showed up in an inebriated state; and it wasn't a good scene. The two guys started wrestling while in their underwear. And, we noticed one of them had literally pooped in his pants during the scuffle. Before we knew it, poop was on a bed and in the floor, and the guy went into the bathroom to clean up after we had enough of that foolishness. About 10 minutes later we found him sitting on the sink in the bathroom, thinking it was the toilet.

To make matters worse, one of us decided to pour Brut cologne on top of the poop to mask the smell. We thought it would be our love nectar to attract good looking coeds. After a few minutes, we realized it sure didn't help, and the stench was overwhelming. The sober members of the gang that night slept out on the balcony of the room, while the two fifty-cent-mixed-drink guys passed out in the funk that involved Brut and poop. If only I had had a camera the next morning when they woke up in the middle of that mess.

We should have tipped room service one hundred dollars for dealing with that situation; they probably had to have decontamination suits to do their work.

I am actually thankful for that night; it pretty much ended any chance of me getting too involved with alcohol for the rest of my life.

On the long ride back, it really hit me for the first time that I was unemployed. The door at WTBC had slammed shut, and I had to figure out what to do next. I had college tuition to pay.

And, literally before I had much time to think about it, a prayer I didn't even have time to pray was answered. I called home from a payphone somewhere in North Florida to let my mom know I had survived the trip, and she said I had a message from Jan Jeffries at WSGN radio in Birmingham. He wanted me to call. Needless to say, I put more coins in the machine and made that call.

Jan was the program director at the top 40 music station in Birmingham, one of the two big time stations in the market. The other was WERC. He told me he heard I had left WTBC and wanted to know if I would come to work for him--not full time, but there would be plenty of hours on weekends and overnights if I wanted them. I took up his offer on the phone, and my unemployment surely didn't last long. And, I was to make $8.00 per hour at the BIG 610. I didn't know what to do with the money I would make that summer. I mean, I hit the jackpot!

My first shift at WSGN was on a Saturday morning in the summer of 1976 working 6 am to 12 noon. I got there early, about 5:00 and it was pure magic. WSGN was located in the penthouse of the City Federal Building in downtown Birmingham. Being up on top of that 27-floor building, the radio station was like the top of a palace. The view over the city was stunning, and the studio, newsroom, and production room were a huge upgrade from my days at the 15th Street School of Broadcasting in Tuscaloosa at WTBC.

I had a news anchor with me that morning, Tony Bruno. The guy had a really deep, professional voice, and I must admit I felt a little out of place. Tony would go on to have a great career in sports talk in Philadelphia and on national radio with ESPN and Fox Sports.

One Saturday morning later in the summer of 1976 a guy walked into the studio; I knew he looked familiar. He said he was meeting station manager, Ben McKinnon to discuss a new record he'd just made. I put two plus two together and realized it was none other than Rick Dees, who had worked at WSGN earlier that decade. He was working at WMPS radio in Memphis at the time and was a big time radio talent. He would soon leave for Los Angeles, where he would have a long, successful career.

Dees pulled me into the production room and played his record for me, asking my opinion. The song was called "Disco Duck," and quite frankly, I thought it was trash. But, I was totally intimidated and told Rick it was really funny and would take off. Deep down in my gut, I wondered if any radio program directors in their right minds would even think about playing that.

Turns out I was dead wrong. Later in the year, I recall seeing Rick and his cast of idiots singing and dancing to that song on national television. I still occasionally hear it played today on oldies stations.

My favorite shift that summer was Saturday nights . . . 6 to midnight. The phones were ringing non-stop, while the music was all rock and roll and up-tempo. Jan had told me to "cook my fanny off" when I worked Saturday night. It was high energy and nothing but fun for a 20-year-old who was literally on top of the city of Birmingham. I was a screaming, top 40 jock on a big boss radio station--way too much fun!

When I worked the overnight shift during the week, I got a chance to see the morning team, Tommy Charles (T.C.) and John Ed. They came in as I left about 5:00. . .there wasn't much interaction between us since I was still an introvert and those guys were focused on show prep. But we developed a good relationship that summer, and I became close friends with Tommy Charles later in my life. We often laughed about our random 5:00 a.m. chats during the summer of 1976.

Deep into August, about the time the fall semester was to start, I wondered how the Birmingham job would mesh with classes in Tuscaloosa. And, while WSGN was truly a showcase, I was a little homesick. I missed my friends at WTBC.

I met with Dave Baird, who was the program director, and he told me he would try to get me back home. It was going to take some serious negotiation with station owner Bert Bank, but he would give it a shot. Long story short, Dave talked Bert into letting me come back, and I went back on the air in Tuscaloosa on the BIG 1230 right as the fall semester started in September 1976, working the 12:00 noon to 3 p.m. shift on weekdays. I am thankful to this day to Dave for going to bat for me and to Bert for taking me back into the family.

I remember the first song I played on that first shift at WTBC in the fall of 1976 was "Lowdown" by Boz Scaggs. Funny the little things in life we recall so many years later.

CHAPTER 8
WATCHING THE STORMS AND
PLAYING THE HITS

We had so many severe weather events in Alabama in the 1970s, but the Birmingham metro was not directly impacted by most of them through 1976. But, the luck of the largest city in the state would run out before the end of the decade.

On April 4, 1977, an F5 tornado tore through the northern part of the city, killing 22 and injuring well over 100. It is called the Smithfield tornado since much of the most serious damage was in the Smithfield Estates neighborhood, just west of I-65 and north of downtown Birmingham. It seemed like every part of Alabama would have its day with severe storms and tornadoes during the decade of the 1970s. It was wild in so many ways.

Due to my work schedule at WTBC, I wasn't able to get away and work disaster relief with the amateur radio guys in Birmingham. But the locals did a superb job in the days and weeks following that disaster. I will never forget listening to the guys on the 146.88 MHz repeater in Birmingham working that horrible tragedy.

J.B. Elliott would tell me years later that Dr. Theodore Fujita, the famous tornado researcher who developed the "F Scale" for rating the strength of a tornado, seriously considered classifying that tornado an F6.

The radio job at WTBC was good. I was getting better and was promoted to program director in the summer of

1977 when Dave decided he just wanted to be a morning personality. Soon after that, I had an interesting phone call and another decision to make.

A guy named Gabby Bruce called me at home one night. He was program director of WNUE radio in Fort Walton Beach, Florida, and wanted me to come down there to work. Boy did that sound appealing. After all, their station, AM-1400, was the Boss of the Beach. I would live in paradise, playing the hits every day with beach babes listening and knowing the sun would be on my shoulder and my toes could be in the sand--in the words of the Stephen Bishop song, "On and On."

If I had accepted that job, my life could have been a total disaster. I would have probably turned into the guy Jimmy Buffett sings about--wastin' away and searching for my lost shaker of salt. I passed and stayed on the radio in Tuscaloosa.

I should mention that the summer of 1977 was the "Tanfastic" summer at WTBC. . .an amazingly creative radio promotion with some really tacky prizes. We gave away six packs of soda and sun tan lotion, and the grand prize was a hammock -- a cheap one at that. But, people were listening, we were having fun, and Bert Bank was making a nice profit.

But, deep in the back of my mind, I knew FM was coming on strong, and our days as Tuscaloosa's top music station were numbered. The days of Top 40 AM radio were really special, and I was blessed to be there at the right place, at the right time.

Most of the legendary AM stations are now news-talk, or they have simply gone dark and are off the air. Even FM music stations are struggling since most folks listen to the music they like using their digital devices. Radio, like just about everything else, has been disrupted by the Internet and digital communication.

CHAPTER 9
LAUNCH OF THE TV CAREER

In the spring of 1978, I was at the top of my game on WTBC, playing the hits. It was a part of my life; after all, with the exception of the summer of 1976, I had been there almost five years or about one quarter of my life. I was still the program director, about the highest position for an on-air person. And, my shift was afternoon drive . . . 3 to 7 p.m. I thought our station sounded like it belonged in a much larger market than Tuscaloosa. Dave Baird was still doing mornings. He had the big, booming pipes and could have worked anywhere. Dave left radio for television in the early 1980s, and as most people know, we would be reunited in 1996 when ABC 33/40 formed. Dave retired from his position as lead news anchor in 2017.

I thought WTBC really sounded fantastic for a smaller market station. Dave Dickson worked middays and Tim Gardner, who went on to be television news director at some great stations, was our news man.

As I recall, my salary was up to $2.25 per hour with that fancy PD title, and life was good. As I pondered things like the coming death of Top 40 AM radio, I received a phone call from Stan Siegal in May of 1978. Stan was the manager of the local Tuscaloosa CBS TV affiliate, WCFT, Channel 33. It was an intriguing phone call; he wanted to know if I was interested in becoming their news anchor for the 6:00 and 10:00 p.m. weeknight newscasts. The duties would include anchoring weather, as well as news, on the late show.

Having an intense interest in weather, the anchoring weather thing was a remarkable possibility. Stan knew I had no formal training in meteorology, but he told me he would often listen to me on WTBC during severe weather, and he thought I would be good at doing weather on television. Never thought about doing news. . . I had no education in journalism and was a horrible writer.

During my initial visit with Stan at the WCFT studio, adjacent to I-59/20 in the eastern part of Tuscaloosa, he hired me on the spot. Like WTBC, I had no resume and never filled out a job application. As stated earlier, I have never had a resume, and I have never filled out a job application to this day. I must be the Forrest Gump of the new millennium or something. I could live my life over thousands of times, and this would never happen again. It is a blessing. And I don't take it for granted.

My last day on WTBC was Friday, June 23, 1978. My mom recorded most of that four-hour show (3 to 7 p.m.) on a cassette recorder, and I am so thankful. I still have that audio, and it brings back warm memories when I play it. The first song on the shift was "The Last Time" by the Rolling Stones, and last one (my last song to play on BIG 1230) was "American Pie" by Don McLean. Dave Baird called me on the air before that last song to say goodbye, but we would be reunited later in the world of television. My news man during the show was Tim Gardner, who would also go into television, winding up as news director at a number of great stations around the country.

The WTBC studio during my time there was on 15th Street in Tuscaloosa across from Forest Lake. The tower in the field behind the station was blown down by Hurricane Frederic in September 1979, and the concrete block building was barely missed by a horrible EF-4 tornado in 2011. Fortunately, the station had moved out of the building in 1990s. In 2012 it was torn down. Today an ocean of apartments sits on the old WTBC property. Still, that spot will always be the birth of my broadcasting career. And, I will always cherish those days.

In the summer of 1978, the movie *Grease*, starring John Travolta and Olivia Newton-John, was released. . . serial killer David Berkowitz, the "Son of Sam," was sentenced to 365 years in prison . . . Jimmy Carter was the President of the United States . . . "Shadow Dancing" by Andy Gibb was the number one song. . .and James Spann first did the weather on television on June 26, 1978.

Channel 33 was a classic small market station; one person wore many hats. I anchored news at 6:00 and 10:00, anchored weather at 10:00, and did a variety of other duties, including shooting news video and writing. I turned 22 years old in the summer of 1978, weighed about 150 pounds, and had zero television experience. I am very thankful that to my knowledge, there are no saved video tapes of my work then since it was pretty rough. My salary was up to $1.90 per hour, and I actually had to worry about suits and ties. I don't think most TV news anchors are at that level today.

In fact, on my first day on the job at Channel 33 as I was getting dressed, it dawned on me that I didn't know how to tie a tie. My mom had purchased a few for me, and after about 10 minutes I was about ready to give up. I didn't have a father to teach me, my mom knew nothing about it, and Google didn't exist. I was too embarrassed to ask anyone at the TV station to help me; thankfully after about 30 minutes of experimentation, I had something that loosely looked correct. Thankfully, after the late news, a production person took me aside and taught me about Windsor Knots.

My life should have ended in September of 1978 while I was at TV 33.

On Tuesday afternoon, September 19, there was scanner traffic about some kind of traffic accident along I-59/20 southwest of Tuscaloosa, near the Black Warrior River. I was dispatched to the scene to shoot video of the wreck; it turned out to be a minor situation as a pickup truck hit a bridge abutment. An Alabama State Trooper was there, along with a wrecker. This really wasn't a news story, but I knew I needed to shoot video of the scene one way or another.

I pulled over on the side of the Interstate and pulled out the camera and recorder. This was very early in the Electronic News Gathering, or ENG phase of TV news (with bulky equipment). I was very surprised when I attempted to turn on the camera and was notified the battery was too low for the camera to function. I had charged this battery, along with another one, to capacity earlier in the day. It made no sense to get a low battery indication. So, I pulled out the second battery and, just like the first one, the indication was that the battery charge was too low for the camera to operate.

Totally unbelievable. Two fully charged batteries somehow magically discharged while I was driving ten miles down the road to that wreck. I was getting a bit angry as I put the equipment back into the back of my car. We didn't have station news cars so we drove our personal vehicles, which in my case was a Datsun 280Z. About the time I closed the hatch, I heard the roar of a runaway 18-wheeler coming down the Interstate at a high rate of speed. Within seconds, that big rig crashed into the State Trooper car, the truck that hit the bridge, and the wrecker. They all exploded.

I jumped into the car and called the police via the amateur radio transceiver in my car (this was before cell phones), and then tried to find out who needed help. As paramedics arrived and I had a chance to gather my thoughts, it became perfectly clear that I should have died instantly. If one of those batteries had been functioning, I would be shooting video of the original wreck with my back to that 18-wheeler, and I would have died instantly. There is no doubt in mind there was some kind of miracle here, some reason I needed to live past September 19, 1978.

I have done many things in my life since that day, and I have no idea why I was kept here. I do know one possible reason; my grandmother died two days before this happened, and perhaps God wanted to spare my mother the pain of having to bury her mom and son at the same time. I attended my grandmother's funeral the next day, September 20.

I stayed at Channel 33 through the summer and early fall of 1978, soaking up knowledge of the television business like a sponge.

CHAPTER 10
BIGGER MARKET; LEGENDARY STATION

I had been working in the radio and television business for five years in the fall of 1978. The first year I was a senior in high school; for the rest of the time I worked while attending college at the University of Alabama. Most of that time was spent in the College of Engineering. I fully thought I would graduate and work for a power company or some other business that needed a good electrical engineer. But, all along my true passions were weather and communicating that information to the public, whether on commercial radio, TV, or ham radio. Nobody ever told me it was a viable career option, and I surely figured at some point in my life, sooner than later, I would have to get a real job and stop having fun.

Most of my high school classmates graduated in May 1978. I did not since I took fewer hours per semester so I could work at the radio station. So, in the fall of 1978, I was still taking classes at the University of Alabama (UA) and working in broadcasting, but now on the television side.

While walking to class one day, I was passing by the Ferguson Center, the student center, on the University of Alabama campus, and saw Bob Howell walking out of the building. Bob's face was very familiar to me; he was the news anchor at WSFA-TV in Montgomery, which at the time clearly had the best news operation in the state. We could get Channel 12 on the cable system in Tuscaloosa, and I watched that channel whenever possible since those broadcasters were so professional and the product looked so good.

WSFA was the only TV station we could receive when I lived in Greenville as a young child. The people on the air at that station were almost like old friends.

I was getting over my shyness in those days, and I went right up to Bob and introduced myself. Bob was very kind to give me a few minutes of his time. I shared a little of my story and that one of my dreams was to work for WSFA one day. He then told me there might be an opening or two in the news department and to call Clarke Edwards, the news director.

I was on the phone with Clarke later that afternoon, and the next week I was in his office. Montgomery is about 90 miles southeast of Tuscaloosa, and while I was making the drive down U.S. 82, many things crossed through my mind. Would they actually consider hiring a 22-year-old kid with five months experience in TV? My dream job was weather, but what if the opening was for news or sports? Was I really good enough to work at WSFA? What would I do about college if they offered me a job?

I saw a small barbeque stand on the side of the road between Maplesville and Prattville on the way down and stopped by for some food to calm my nerves. The place was called "Jim's Pit Barbeque," and to this very day it is my favorite BBQ joint in the state. Jim Lenoir owned it in 1978 when I first made the discovery; his daughter

Jeanette now runs the place. I still stop by anytime I am close.

I nervously listened to Clarke Edwards in his office at WSFA on 10 East Delano Street in Montgomery. The opening? Weekend sports anchoring, and weekday sports reporting. My heart dropped since I basically knew nothing about journalism or sports reporting, but oddly enough, he offered me the job on the spot. Knowing I needed the TV experience and understanding the chance of a lifetime to be on the anchor desk at Channel 12 at such a young age, I accepted.

I moved to Montgomery in late October, 1978; my new home was a small apartment on Woodley Road, just south of the Southern Bypass. Steve Young wrote a song about Woodley Road, "The Seven Bridges Road," in 1969, and two years after my time spent there, the Eagles would make the song famous. And yes, Woodley Road does have seven bridges and moss-covered trees.

That was the first time away from my mom; I lived at home during those college years in Tuscaloosa. I had no idea if I could really anchor sports, or if I was good enough to work at WSFA, but I knew I needed to seize the opportunity.

My colleagues on the weekend anchor team were Norman Lumpkin, who handled news, and Mack Carmack, the weatherman. Norman was a legendary journalist, one of the first African-American newsmen on Alabama television, and a very talented investigative reporter. I am not sure Norman enjoyed anchoring the news, but he loved going after the hard stories. Both Norman and Mack became good friends, and we shared many fun times and laughs together. I cherish their friendships to this day.

Our most famous outing came in early 1979; we decided to go to dinner at Quincy's on the Southern Bypass after the 6:00 news one Saturday night. The place was crowded, as expected, and Norman, who was driving a station news car, pulled up right by the door and parked in a handicapped space. Understand, the idea of handicapped parking was brand new in 1979, and Norman didn't totally understand the serious nature of parking in one of those blue spaces without a decal or special tag.

Norman, being the stubborn person he was, never relented after Mack and I tried to talk him out of parking there. Now understand, I was 22 years old at the time and sometimes didn't make the best decisions. That was one of those times. As we got out of the car, I told Norman and Mack that if we parked there, then we needed to be handicapped. Next, before we knew it, the three of us did indeed act as though we were handicapped walking into the restaurant. We enjoyed a great meal and headed back to 10 East Delano without thinking about the parking place or our dramatic entrance.

Turns out one person at Quincy's noticed our act and didn't really appreciate it. She wrote a letter to the editor of the *Montgomery Advertiser*, one of the daily newspapers in town, and the paper printed it a few weeks later. The caption said, "A Night On The Town" . . . and the lady went on to share how she saw these three well-dressed men getting out of a car by the door "acting as though they were handicapped." She was shocked and disgusted at our behavior and even more disturbed when she saw those same three men on WSFA TV News later that night at 10:00!

Needless to say, station management was not happy. Thankfully for me, Norman was the only one called into the front office since he was driving. And, most people in town thought it was weekday anchors Bob Howell, Phil Snow, and Dan Atkinson since the letter didn't specify that it happened on a Saturday night. I felt badly for Norman since I was the one that suggested the idea, but he just blew it off and told me not to worry about it.

I should mention the weeknight anchors made me feel very welcome, and it was especially a thrill to work in the same building with Dan Atkinson, who quite frankly was the best weather person in the state--at least to my knowledge--and a fantastic role model. I studied him both on the air and off the air. He was kind and always willing to spend some time with me.

Through a series of odd circumstances, I actually got to anchor weather on Channel 12 a number of times in the spring of 1979. There was no doubt in my mind this was my calling; I did learn to enjoy sports reporting, but it just wasn't my passion. I covered Alabama and Auburn basketball, Montgomery Rebels' baseball, and special events like the George Lindsey Celebrity Golf Tournament. I especially liked covering the Rebels; baseball was always interesting to me, and the environment at Paterson Field was great. I never dreamed

I would watch my son pitch on that same mound in tournaments later in life.

CHAPTER 11
BACK TO RADIO ONE FINAL TIME

It was late May of 1979, and I was contacted by some folks from WHHY radio in Montgomery. They knew of my days at WTBC in Tuscaloosa and had an opening for the afternoon shift for their FM station, Y-102. I should say that every person I spoke with about that opportunity told me not to do it. WSFA was the big station in Alabama, and I should have opportunities there to ultimately get into weather and move up the ladder. Consensus was that moving back to radio in Montgomery could be a career ender, and the dream of doing weather on television would die.

To this day, I honestly don't know why, but I took the radio offer. I started just before I turned 23 on June 6, 1979.

WHHY-AM was another legendary station programmed by Larry Stevens. FM music formatted stations were zooming past the AM guys in the late 1970s, and this was a chance to get in on their FM station and the rapidly growing audience. With that job I would get weekends off (other than an occasional remote or special station event), my hours would be from 10:00 a.m. until 7:00 p.m., and I would get a big raise to $200 per week.

The summer of 1979 would turn out to be one of the most carefree, fun times of my life. I guess radio was still in my blood, and working afternoons at Y-102 was a blast. I loved coming over to the studios on Norman Bridge Road and playing the hits on the FM side, where there is no static at all. I was playing songs by Supertramp, the Electric Light Orchestra, the Atlanta Rhythm Section, Earth, Wind, and Fire, Wet Willie, and The Knack.

I was having a blast at the same time and did ponder the future. I had dropped out of college to take the WSFA job and autumn was coming. I thought about enrolling at Auburn University-Montgomery while working at Y-102 and wondered what in the world my major needed to be. I didn't really think much about meteorology since the dream seemed so far away at that point. The idea of a television weather career seemed an impossible dream. I had no formal education in meteorology and very limited experience.

While it was great fun, I also knew a long-term radio career would not be especially healthy for me and future family life. Many in radio moved around from station to station since in the radio business you are usually fired within a few years, or even months, lived a less-than-Godly life, and tended to self-destruct. But, I chose to enjoy the moment. I am still thankful to Larry Stevens and the crew for giving me this opportunity; I often tell people today that it was the last time I got some sleep. It was after all the good 'ole summer of 1979, when I didn't have to come in until 10:00 a.m.

Just three months into my career at Y-102, there came another life changing phone call out of the blue. The call was from Ed Clark, who had worked with me at Channel 33 in Tuscaloosa the year before. Ed had moved on to WAPI-TV, the NBC station in Birmingham. He asked me "Why in the world are you back in radio?" and told me that the station was putting together a new weeknight anchor team for the fall. And, the news director, Wendell Harris, wanted to speak with me about the weather position.

After picking myself off the floor, I told Ed I would be happy to speak with Mr. Harris. I remembered him from being the news anchor on Channel 13 back in the 1960s; he had covered all of the historic Civil Rights events in Birmingham during that turbulent decade.

On an early August morning in 1979, I made the drive up I-65 and sat down with Wendell and the management team at WAPI. Channel 13 was a distant second place station to WBRC-TV in the local ratings, and after talking with them I knew they were being serious about upgrading their product. They had a good, young anchor team in place; Ken Snow and Pam Huff. Pam and I would go on to work together for many years. For sports, they were bringing in Scott Palmer, who had big market talent, but the missing piece of the puzzle for them was a weather anchor. Ed was the one who recommended me for that position to the big shots at Channel 13.

I must admit that it was pretty cool being on the top of Red Mountain in Birmingham, where all of the TV stations were located, right by the Vulcan statue and with such a great view of the city.

A newspaper ad for the WVTM-TV (Channel 13) news team in 1981.

This time I wasn't hired on the spot. Instead, I had to go on their big blue wall (most stations used blue for the chroma-key walls back in the 1970s), record several weather segments, and interact with their anchor team. I must admit that I was scared to death. The fact that they were even talking to me was beyond belief, and for me, this was my one shot at starting the dream career I thought was out of reach.

In the days following this interview, I was back on the air at Y-102 wondering where all of this was going. Would they call me back? Why in the world would a station in a market the size of Birmingham hire a 23-year-old with little experience? I really didn't share this with many people since it would be embarrassing if I didn't get the job. In my mind, the chances weren't very high.

A day or two went by, and there was no call from Birmingham. I figured I had gotten so close to my dream job, but it just passed by like a ship in the night. I had pretty much given up; I was ready to keep playing the hits at Y-102 and look for some kind of new college major that would bring me a good career.

But then the phone rang. It was Wendell Harris offering me the job--primarily, weeknight weather anchor at WAPI-TV in Birmingham. I don't think I even asked about the salary; I just said YES! Turns out, I made about $25,000 in that first year, which sure seemed like a lot of money to me.

Larry and the gang at WHHY/Y-102 were very understanding. They gave me a summer of fun and carefree living, and I hope I gave them some high energy, on-air talent for the afternoon drive slot on the new FM. This effectively ended my radio career as a rock and roll jock, although I must confess, I did drive back to Montgomery on a few Saturdays in 1980 to work weekend shifts for Larry, this time on the AM station. One the guys at Channel 13 found out I was doing a little weekend moonlighting on the radio in Montgomery; the bosses kindly asked me to stop. I understood.

I honestly can't recall the last time I opened up the WHHY microphone; I would say sometime on a Saturday morning in the late summer of 1980. You see, radio always stays in your blood. I was able to be a jock at big boss radio stations in Tuscaloosa, Birmingham, and Montgomery during the peak of the Top 40 era.

CHAPTER 12
BIRMINGHAM TV WEATHER CAREER KICKS OFF WITH A HURRICANE

I started my employment at Channel 13 in Birmingham on Monday, September 10, 1979. I would be replacing long-time weather anchor Rosemary Lucas, who was being reassigned to a new position as a news reporter. That was the end of an era on Birmingham television; for many years Rosemary did weather on Channel 13, and Pat Gray was the weather anchor over on Channel 6, WBRC. It was in the late 1970s when local stations decided to get more serious about television news and weather; Mike Royer was brought in at Channel 6, and I was the new man at Channel 13.

Another sign of the times was Channel 13's color radar, a new radar receiver made by Enterprise Electronics of Enterprise, Alabama. This radar enabled us to show radar in full color for the first time. The radar data came from the National Weather Service WSR-57 facility in Bibb County, near Brent. Although the original radar had been destroyed by the May 27, 1973, F4 tornado, it had fortunately been replaced.

The plan was for me to first appear on the air on Monday September 17; that would give me one week to meet the staff, learn the equipment, and get ready for the biggest TV job of my life. There actually wasn't much equipment to learn; we had the Enterprise radar receiver and a National Oceanic Atmospheric Administration (NOAA) weather wire (an old teletype machine), and that was about it. You see, back in 1979 we drew fronts, highs, and lows on big maps on the studio wall covered by Plexiglas. If you did television weather, you also had to be somewhat of an artist.

That first day was full of emotion and adrenaline for me, but at the same time, I was also focused on what was going on along the southern coast of Cuba. Hurricane Frederic was on a path that would take it into the Gulf of Mexico, and there was no doubt it could become a big player for somebody on the Central Gulf Coast. I had a long discussion with News Director Wendell Harris about the storm and suggested he make plans for coverage in case the Alabama coast was involved.

On day two, Tuesday, September 11, it became clear that the Alabama Gulf Coast would indeed be at risk. In fact, the forecast from the National Hurricane Center put the storm right up into Mobile Bay late the following night, September 12. Wendell had a decision to make . . . whether to put me on the air with the other anchors earlier than planned or send me to the coast.

The decision was made to send me south, to either Mobile or Baldwin County, the two Alabama coastal counties. I was informed that afternoon, and I went to the small apartment I had leased to pack and get ready for the trip.

Understand, it was a different world in 1979. No cell phones, no commercial Internet, no satellite trucks. Needless to say, that hurricane coverage was going to be a huge challenge for a 23-year-old rookie.

My photographer was Dwayne Syltie, who grew up in Mobile and was a great choice since he knew the territory. We left Red Mountain early Wednesday morning, September 12. WAPI actually used station wagons for news vehicles in 1979, and we pushed that thing to the limit on the way south along I-65. My heart was pumping on the drive; I wasn't sure if the station wanted coverage, or wanted to get rid of me by putting me in the path of a Category 3 hurricane.

We got into Mobile and stopped at a payphone to call the station (remember, no cell phones, and the two-way radio worked only around Birmingham). Landfall was to come early the next morning, during the pre-dawn hours on September 13, and the decision was made to keep me in the city of Mobile. The goal was to have me broadcast live via telephone during the 10:00 p.m. news. If we went down to the coast, places like Gulf Shores, Orange Beach, or Dauphin Island, there was a good chance there would be no phone service. We would make our home for the night at the Azalea Middle School in Mobile, which also served as an evacuation center. I would guess there were at least 300 people there, including residents of a nearby senior adult facility.

Back at the station, we had a new portable microwave system that allowed us to go live locally. Pam Huff was sent to the National Weather Service office at 11 West Oxmoor Road for a live shot at 10:00; she would interview long-time National Weather Service (NWS) meteorologist Harold Quattlebaum after my live phone report from Mobile.

Frederic actually made landfall on the western end of Dauphin Island during the 10:00 news as a strong Category 3 on the Saffir-Simpson hurricane intensity scale. A weather station at the top of the Dauphin Island Bridge recorded a peak wind gust of 145 mph and through the night winds in Mobile gusted from 100 to 130 mph.

It was a loud, chaotic night at the Azalea Middle School as the hurricane roared up Mobile Bay. Memories of my experience with Hurricane Eloise immediately came into my mind because of the noise. In and of itself--this ferocious, intense, howling blowing sound all night--could drive anyone crazy. Then, about 2:00 a.m. part of the roof came off, and many of the elderly evacuees had to be moved to other parts of the school building. Some of them were injured during that process, and a few physicians in the building had to attend to them using our television lights; the power had been off for hours.

The screaming wind finally started to die down about daybreak, the morning of September 13, and it was then our job to go out and shoot video and tell the story. Remember, there was no way for us to get video back to Birmingham, so we had about three hours to get the job done, and then we had to make the five-hour drive back to Birmingham so we could edit and get the story on the evening newscasts. Dwayne made it happen. The two of us, with no sleep, pulled into the WAPI TV parking lot shortly before 4:00 in the afternoon, and the first story made it to air at 5:00.

Younger photographers have no idea what this was like with today's technology and communication abilities. We shot this event on three-quarter inch tape using cameras and recorders that were as heavy as boat anchors. The editing process was slow as molasses, and we just prayed our tapes didn't get stuck in the machines, which looked like some kind of Rube Goldberg contraption.

After the 6:00 news, News Director Wendell Harris unveiled a secret and the coverage plan for the following day. WAPI was going to announce the following week that a new helicopter was coming into the station's arsenal at a big station function. But, considering the circumstances, station management decided to forget the big ceremony and just put the chopper into use for this big story. Dwayne and I were going to fly down to Mobile Thursday morning in that new helicopter for more coverage. We were ordered to get some sleep and be at a helipad down the mountain, closer to the UAB campus. We were about to hop on board at the first light of day for the ride down to Mobile.

With the helicopter, the five-hour drive was cut down to an 80-90 minute flight. We had plenty of time to tell more stories and shoot more video. And, of course, from the air, see the big picture. There was plenty of damage to see in Mobile, but we took "Sky 13" down to the coast, and our jaws dropped. The storm surge just about wiped out Gulf Shores, Orange Beach, and Dauphin Island. And I do mean wiped out. The bridge connecting Dauphin Island to the mainland was literally blown away, and as far as we could see, homes, businesses, and other buildings were severely damaged, or just washed away.

We landed at Jack Edwards Airport in Gulf Shores and arranged for ground transportation to cover the arrival of President Jimmy Carter, who was there to see the damage for himself. The rebuilding process that was started after Hurricane Frederic was the initialization of the rapid growth and buildup of our Alabama's coastline. in coming years, what were small vacation getaway towns and fishing villages would become world class tourist destinations with miles and miles of high rise hotels and condos. That time, we could keep working until mid-afternoon. The short flight back in the chopper was a God send. Our stories and video that night were so much better. We did a 30-minute special on Hurricane Frederic later that month.

CHAPTER 13
NEWS TEAM, ASSEMBLE!

During the late 1970s and early 1980s, most local TV stations were in the process of doing a serious upgrade to their news operations after determining that they could easily be a profit center. This was before CNN, Fox News, MSNBC, the Drudge Report, and Huffington Post. Local television newscasts and newspapers were not only relevant to the masses but were the only way of getting the news of the day.

On the TV side, new hires were actually trained journalists (as opposed to announcers), and fancy new equipment was coming into play, like electronic news gathering (ENG), microwave trucks, and helicopters like "Sky 13." Anchor teams were being heavily promoted by local stations, and brandings like "Eyewitness News" and "Total News" were commonplace. At Channel 13, we were the "Action News Team," consisting of news anchors Huff and Snow, sports anchor Palmer, and weatherman Spann. We were all young, in our 20s--but we were good friends and bonded in the TV newsroom environment. In fact, Ken Snow became my roommate the next year, in 1980. We lived in an apartment complex on Valley Avenue, just a couple of miles west of the station on the south slope of Red Mountain.

We were somewhat of an odd couple; Ken was an outgoing ladies man and liked the nightlife Birmingham offered after completion of the 10:00 news. I was still very much an introvert, preferring to get on the ham radio bands and talk to my tech buddies as opposed to spending a night on the town.

I recall one night, after some pressure, I went with Ken to a few late-night honky tonks. He was driving initially, but I would later become the driver after he consumed a number of adult beverages. We finally made it home about the time the sun came up . . . that was the last time I went out with Ken in only one car.

Ken was from Texas, and late at night we always had to listen to WBAP-AM in Fort Worth, Texas, a clear channel 50,000-watt station that could easily be picked up in Alabama after dark. The midnight show featuring Bill Mack was one of his favorites, giving him a taste of home. Again, I had no idea I would be working in the Dallas/Fort Worth TV market just a few years later, competing against Harold Taft, who did the weather on Bill's show and was the one Bill called "The World's Greatest Weatherman."

I did enjoy my time with Ken as a friend, co-worker, and roommate and was so saddened to hear of his death in May 2015. We had so many laughs together.

The Channel 13 newsroom had some interesting people. The assistant news directors were Barry Copeland and Tom Roberts, and one of the primary newscast producers was a guy named Jimmy Carter (no, not the former president). Carter was nothing short of a wild man, but he had a fantastic sense of the news business and could handle breaking news better than anyone else. Later in his career he went on camera, working for The Nashville

Network for many years, and for the NBC affiliate in Nashville, WSMV, Channel 4. Jimmy had his roots in Montgomery radio, much like me. We had much in common and remain good friends today.

Our primary competition was next door on Red Mountain; the guys at WBRC, Channel 6 were number one. Legendary newsman Joe Langston was their lead anchor, Herb Winches did sports, and Mike Royer handled weather for the "Total News" team. It was a heated battle for ratings, which continues to this very day.

A couple of years later, in 1981, a talent raid would change the local landscape in a huge way. I was listening to one of the local news-talk stations on radio, WERC, while driving in from Tuscaloosa, where I did a weather program for elementary school students. The lead story was that the Channel 6 News family was getting a divorce, and that Joe Langston and Herb Winches were headed to Channel 13. I almost ran off the road, and needless to say, I picked up the pace, heading rapidly to Red Mountain to find out what was going on. It wasn't a good scene; anchors were being called in one at a time to the office of Wendell Harris. I didn't know if I was being fired or who I would be working with that night.

Turns out that Pam Huff and I made the cut and were staying, but it was true, Joe Langston and Herb Winches were indeed changing channels. That was quite the gamble for station owner Times Mirror, but it paid off. Within a few months, Channel 13 jumped to the top of the local ratings with the team of Huff, Langston, Winches, and Spann.

The television news business is harsh. Your job security depends on ratings and accordingly, how people perceive you. Being fired is just part of it. Scott Palmer did just fine; he went on to have a long career as a sports anchor in Philadelphia, a much larger market, and Ken Snow went back home to his beloved Texas.

Oddly enough, just two years later, Joe and Herb would go back to Channel 6, and Gene Lively would come in as Pam's new co-anchor. Ken Lass was introduced as the new sports anchor in 1983. As you can see, Pam and I tended to be the glue that kept the anchor team together simply because of our staying power.

There were other changes as Times Mirror tended to move people around. Wendell Harris was promoted to General Manager at their station in Austin, Texas (KTBC, Channel 7), and Barry Copeland didn't stay too long as the new news director since he was promoted to the news director position at KTVI, Channel 2, in St. Louis, another Times Mirror station. We called it the Times Mirror carousel. I had no idea I would take a ride on it in 1984.

CHAPTER 14
WEATHER TECHNOLOGY IN THE
EARLY DAYS

My first night to anchor the weather on WAPI-TV was Monday, September 17, 1979. To this day I don't know what I did with all the free time I had. I had to anchor the weather only on the 6:00 and 10:00 p.m. newscasts weekdays. There was no radio weather work to handle at the time, no blogs, no social media. Just two weather segments on television, five nights a week.

The "Action News 13" Weather Station consisted of a NOAA Weather Wire, the Enterprise color radar receiver, and a big U.S. national map covered in Plexiglas. The weather wire was a teletype circuit to the National Weather Service in Birmingham, which at the time was at 11 West Oxmoor Road, about four miles southwest of the station. I must confess that sometimes I miss the sound of those teletype machines clacking away; I just about memorized the sound they made when the regular circuit was interrupted by a severe weather watch from the old Severe Storms Forecast Center in Kansas City (SELS) or a warning from Birmingham.

One big problem was that the elements of the weather center weren't close. The teletype was in the newsroom, far from the studio, and the radar receiver was back in master control . . . closer to the studio, but still not convenient. And, my office was on the other end of the building, in an old radio studio formerly occupied by WAPI radio when it was co-located with the TV station. I burned plenty of calories running from point to point during active weather.

When I used radar on the air, I had to rely on another person pressing sector buttons on the radar receiver, which was not only awkward but led to some pretty rough moments when I tried to zoom in on a storm. And, to use a radar other than the Centreville WSR-57, which had a dedicated phone circuit, we had to dial a number to access the data by modem. Also, in most cases, only one user was allowed at a time. During active weather situations, if I wanted another radar, it was a matter of luck if I could get in. Most of the time I heard a busy signal. When trying to access the Brownsville, TX, radar during the approach of Hurricane Allen in August 1980, I bet I got at least 50 busy signals before I finally got through for just one radar image. And, getting the right overlay for those out-of-state radar sites was another challenge. It all makes me so thankful for what we have today.

The biggest daily challenge for me was drawing on that map covered by Plexiglas. My art skill was pretty much on the same level as that of a second grader; just putting highs, lows, and fronts down was not easy. Occasionally I would write words such as "cold," "windy" and "record warmth" on the map, and on the air they looked more like Egyptian hieroglyphics. And, of course, after every TV weathercast I had to clean the map with Windex or some other cleaning solution.

If I didn't clean it up right, the morning weatherman, a guy named Dick Breitenfeld, would fuss about it to management the next day. His name on the air was "Dick

Briet," and he wore a toupee that had seen better days. In his younger years, he opened for Sarah Vaughan, who was signed with the William Morris Agency, and was appearing in Long Island nightclubs. Most of the old school television talent in the 1960s and 1970s had a background in entertainment.

In 1980 our on-air map got an upgrade. Our sister station in Dallas, KDFW-TV, went to a new computer graphics system, and we got its old map. It was larger and better, and I was actually excited to get it because it was magnetic, complete with stick-on highs, lows, fronts, and words. No more drawing on maps and no more Windex after the newscasts.

It was about that time I had an idea. Instead of using old black and white weather satellite loops that were sometimes over 8 hours old and that came down the network news feed in the afternoons, I could drive down to the National Weather Service on Oxmoor Road and get a fresh satellite image from their facsimile machine and use it on the air. So, on most days, I made the drive twice daily for that satellite image. And, best of all, I made some very good friends at the NWS office. I especially loved it when J.B. Elliott was on duty; he would always take time to talk with me, share his knowledge, and let me ask questions. You have to remember that I still had no formal weather training at the time, and I had so much to learn.

Many nights after the 6:00 news I would swing by the Hardee's drive through on the way to the NWS, and we would have Hardee parties, complete with junk food, laughs, weather talk, and stale jokes. I soaked up the knowledge shared by those men (no women were stationed at Birmingham as meteorologists during those years) like a sponge. And to this day I am thankful to them for sharing with me.

Of course, making an accurate weather forecast was the most important part of my job. And, it was quite the challenge in the late 1970s/early 1980s when I was beginning. Numerical Weather Prediction (NWP) was pretty primitive back then; there was one operational regional known as the Limited Fine Mesh model (LFM). It was introduced in 1971 and was pretty much all we had until the Nested Grid Model (NGM) came along in 1987. The LFM had a grid resolution of 190.5 km, which is almost laughable today but was high resolution 35 years ago.

The National Meteorological Center's Global Spectral Model was introduced in August 1980, giving us a look at the entire planet. The LFM and spectral model output were transmitted via Digital Facsimile Charts (DIFAX), a circuit that sent low resolution maps and images to National Weather Service offices and some private sector forecast centers. Unfortunately, Channel 13 didn't have a DIFAX machine, so again trips down to the NWS office on Oxmoor Road were needed to see model output. Putting the daily forecast together was time consuming and quite the adventure.

CHAPTER 15
STARTING A FAMILY

I was never a lady's man. I was not especially athletic, didn't have Robert Redford looks, and was still rather introverted. Rarely having the guts to ask girls out, I was pretty much the guy that worked all the time with little social life. I did get to know a lot of girls during the WTBC days; those were the ones that called the request line. I liked some of them but never had the guts to ask them out.

The first girl I really dated on a steady basis came along in 1979 when I was 23 years old, working that marvelous summer at Y-102 in Montgomery. We kept a long distance relationship for a while after I moved to Channel 13 in Birmingham, but she decided to end it in November of that year. I was dumped right before a friend's wedding; I remember driving to Fort Walton Beach, Florida, by myself after the ceremony to collect my thoughts. I shed some tears along the journey south to the beach, but I sure didn't blame her because I was just not what she needed. First song on the radio was "Babe" by Styx after I turned onto U.S. 331 off the southern bypass in Montgomery on the drive to the beach. Oddly enough, the lead guitar player for the band Styx, Tommy Shaw, is from Montgomery.

Those songs on Top 40 radio stations in the 1970s were the soundtrack of my life. I relate some banner event or memory to almost every song from my wonder years of the 70s,

It was as the calendar turned over to 1980 that Ken Snow and I got that Valley Ridge apartment. Remember that Snow was a real ladies man. That guy had women all over him, and I often got to study the master in action. But, still, I was pretty quiet, introverted, and lacking in the social skills to become a "babe magnet."

Despite those simple truths, I would start dating the love of my life in the fall of 1980.

I first met Karen O'Mary when she had a date with a close friend of mine while we were all in college. She was good looking and had a great personality. I figured I was in so far over my head I would never have the nerve to even talk with her.

Oddly enough, one night Karen called me on the night shift at Channel 13, asking me to do a favor and emcee an event at the University of Alabama. Somehow, I got up the nerve to ask her out, and after she agreed to go out with me on a second date, I felt like there was hope for a longer-term relationship.

Turned out to be a whirlwind romance. Despite getting to know me, and the odd occupation known as television weather, things went very well. And, before we knew it, we were engaged in the spring of 1981. I think the hardest part was asking permission from her father, Paul O'Mary, a retired Army colonel and a very ominous figure. My fear was unfounded; he showed love and support, and I admired this man so much over the years. Colonel O'Mary passed away in 2015, and I greatly miss his wisdom. He was truly a great American who served in

World War II, Korea, and Vietnam. He spoke with President John F. Kennedy several times from the Berlin Wall and ended his Army career at the Pentagon. He went on to serve as the Professor of Military Science at the University of Alabama, which is what brought his family to Tuscaloosa.

Our wedding day. June 6, 1981

The marriage was June 6, 1981, the exact same day I turned 25 years old. Getting married on your birthday is actually a pretty good trick; you never forget your anniversary. During the wedding at the First Baptist Church of Tuscaloosa on that early summer evening, a whopper of a thunderstorm developed right over the city. Perfect way for a weather guy to start a marriage.

Any person married to a broadcast meteorologist is a saint. We work horrible hours in a challenging environment and have to deal with trolls and bizarre co-workers and have the occasional forecast bust that can send us into a tailspin. Karen has learned to handle this life beautifully and with grace over the 38 years we have been married. She is patient, forgiving, and understanding. She makes me laugh and is my best friend.

CHAPTER 16
BANNER WEATHER EVENTS IN THE EARLY 80s

During my five years at Channel 13 (1979-1984), there weren't many big tornado days in Alabama, but there were other banner events that shaped my career. After Hurricane Frederic in 1979, the great Heat Wave of 1980 was the next big threat to those living in my state. On the surface, it doesn't make much sense because every summer around here is brutally hot. But this one stood out in many ways.

On July 10, 1980, Birmingham's high was 101 degrees, our first triple digit of the season. Just for fun, that day I did the weather live from the big freezer at the Piggly Wiggly in Homewood, fully dressed out in a thick jacket and Russian hat. The next day, July 11, the high was 102, and I fried an egg on the sidewalk. Of course, the egg wasn't really fried, but it was just something most TV weather guys try on really hot days. But, while we were chuckling at the egg fry, the people in the news studio were letting me know they were hearing of many heat related cases at local hospital emergency rooms, and that we might want to take more of a serious approach to the intense summer heat.

By July 13 the high at the Birmingham Airport was 106 degrees, only one degree below the city's hottest temperature on record, 107 recorded on July 29, 1930. We went on to have eight consecutive days with triple digit heat.

There would ultimately be 123 heat-related deaths in Alabama during the summer of 1980, with 115 of them coming in late June/July. It is still the modern benchmark for heat waves in Alabama.

Most of those who died were elderly people who lived alone with no air conditioning. It was a big wakeup call for me. I learned that most people who watch me on television don't live where I live, look like I do, and have a different age, culture, and worldview. I was only 24 years old. I knew I had to grow up quickly to be successful on television and to understand what life is like for a 45-year-old mom with three kids, a 72-year-old widow who lives in government housing, and a 55-year-old businessman.

For many of the young interns who come into our office these days, the first thing I do is take them to a Walmart in a working-class part of the city to see if they can communicate with those in other socio-economic groups. They are rarely successful, and it opens their eyes.

I could not imagine what life would be like living without air conditioning in Alabama in the summer, but many do, and some lost their lives in the long, hot summer of 1980.

Eighteen months later, it was just the opposite. January 1982 brought brutal cold; the temperature in Birmingham dropped to 2 degrees above zero on Monday, January 11. The high that Monday afternoon was only 27, and I spent hours in the weather office concerned about a potential winter storm that would impact Alabama and the Deep South. From everything I could see, it sure looked like the event which would be mostly freezing rain with some big-time ice accumulation that would begin the next day, Tuesday, January 12, during the evening or nighttime hours. And, that was the forecast I proclaimed to the state.

The idea was excellent, but the timing was horrible. The freezing rain started about 8 to 10 hours sooner than expected, meaning people were at work and school when the ice storm cranked up. Within literally 30 minutes, ice covered all roads and highways with a very cold infrastructure and frozen ground. By 10:00 that morning, we were living in a real world ice skating rink. And, with everyone trying to get home at once, it turned into a disaster. Remember, everyone was thinking the ice wouldn't be an issue until after 6:00 p.m.

Karen and I lived in Alabaster, about 20 miles south of Channel 13's studio location atop Red Mountain. Seeing the early morning radar trends (actually, hearing about them on NOAA Weather Radio . . . remember, this was before apps and the public Internet), I knew I had to get in early, or else I was going nowhere. I made it into the studio just before 10:00, on roads that were rapidly deteriorating. My heart was beating out of my chest on that horrible drive. I was wondering if I would make it to Red Mountain and if I would be fired for the botched forecast. I was monitoring the local amateur radio repeaters, and it sounded bad. I mean **really** bad!

Thousands abandoned their cars on highways and started walking in random directions, trying to find any warm shelter with food.

As temperatures hovered near the freezing mark Monday night, the freezing rain kept falling and created a thick coating of ice on all exposed objects. Trees snapped, pulling down power lines and putting as many as 750,000 Alabamians in the dark. Some would be without power for over two weeks; this was a true humanitarian crisis.

Travel did become possible for a short while on Wednesday, January 13, as temperatures rose to just above freezing at lunch. But the sound of tree limbs snapping under the weight of the ice was like hearing shotguns, and the break in temperature was very short-lived.

Wednesday night another disturbance brought a nice snow to North/Central Alabama that led to some great sledding and snowball fights on Thursday. But when it was all said and done, twenty Alabamians were dead, and another 300 injured, and damage totaled $78 million. That botched forecast still haunts me today; no doubt the worst of my career--although one in January 2014 came close.

We were stuck at Channel 13 for a part of five days. Most of us arrived during the morning hours on Monday; we were not able to get off the mountain until Friday. And, unfortunately most of us packed clothes for only two days. The men could handle it, but it was especially hard on the women. Food and sleep were in very short supply, and to say that everyone was getting cranky was an understatement. I am just glad we didn't kill each other.

During the week following the historic ice storm, we were taken to the station in special vans with reinforced roofs due to large chunks of melting ice falling from the 1,200-foot tower on the station property on the mountain. The roof at the station had to be completely rebuilt, and we were lucky nobody was hurt. Trust me, ice storms are no fun. And they are still hard to forecast, even with today's technology and forecast advancements.

Severe weather coverage was radically different in the early 1980s. If I needed to do a cut-in for a tornado warning, a booth announcer would announce a weather bulletin, and I would go on briefly, with a quick return to regular programming. There were no wall-to-wall tornado coverages, no SKYCAMs, and no fancy computer graphics. The color radar from the old Enterprise receiver was pretty much all we had.

I believe my longest severe weather coverage on Channel 13 came on December 3, 1983, when a tornado warning was issued for Jefferson County, including the city of Birmingham. From my recollection, I was on the air for at least 30 minutes uninterrupted. But, there was one huge problem. Nobody, and I mean nobody, was watching my coverage. You see, this tornado warning was issued during the annual Iron Bowl college football game between the University of Alabama and Auburn University, and the game was over on the ABC station, WBRC, Channel 6. Those folks didn't have the guts to interrupt the game for weather coverage (I don't blame them, considering the era), but to their credit, they did put a tornado warning message on the top right part of the screen after it was issued.

Legion Field, in the western part of Birmingham, was where the game was played. The public address announcer Simpson Pepper read the warning over the loudspeakers, but the game was not stopped. With ten minutes to go in the game, the rain was coming down in torrents as Auburn tried to control the ball and win the game in the horrible conditions as they clung to a 23-20 lead. The rain began to fall so heavily that people could barely see the field on the cameras.

Fortunately, the storm did not produce a tornado in western Birmingham, or the results would have been catastrophic. But later, the same storm dropped an F3 tornado that heavily damaged the Winn Dixie store at Oxford, east of Birmingham, killing two people. A total of seven tornadoes touched down across the state that afternoon and evening.

Auburn went on to win the game 23-20.

CHAPTER 17
TOP TEN MARKET AT A VERY YOUNG AGE

On Tuesday, July 31, 1984, I was called to the front office at Channel 13. That didn't happen often, and I had to wonder if I was in trouble. The General Manager, Jack Harrison, was at his desk when I walked in and said I had a phone call. Now this was really getting in the weird zone; I had good knowledge the front office was not a phone booth, and the manager was not a phone operator.

After picking up the phone, I heard the voice of John McCrory, who was the President of Times Mirror Broadcasting, the owner of Channel 13. Mr. McCrory told me the company recognized my talent, appreciated my work, and wanted to promote me to the largest station in the chain, KDFW-TV in Dallas. He said he wanted me to fly out to North Texas and meet him for a couple of days so he could show me the station and the market. At the time, I had never been to Dallas, or even to the state of Texas.

So, the next day, I was off to Dallas. I had a lunch meeting with McCrory and Bill Baker, the General Manager of KDFW. Then we went up to Reunion Tower deck, where we could see the sprawling Metroplex. Understand, North Texas, unlike North Alabama, is flat as a pancake, and I could see for miles and miles. I could see the iconic Texas Stadium in Irving, downtown Fort Worth, the tall buildings up in Los Colinas and North Dallas, DFW Airport, and the broadcast towers for the market, clustered on Cedar Hill, south of Dallas.

I must admit that I felt like it was when Satan took Jesus to a very high mountain and showed him all the kingdoms of the world and their splendor. Not that McCrory was Satan and I was Jesus, but the surrounding circumstances seemed to fit. You see, I was born in Alabama, raised in Alabama, and am a home boy. There was an uneasy feeling to this.

Funny, for most in television their goal is to make the big time. Reaching a top ten market as a lead weather anchor is just a daydream for most in the business, and there I was, being moved into that position at the age of 28 without lifting a finger.

Another oddity about that day was that I was not allowed to see the station, although we could just about walk there from Reunion Tower. McCrory and Baker said they were making many changes, from talent to management, and they didn't want to let the cat out of the bag. Also, that afternoon, they asked me to commit and sign a two-year contract. Quite frankly, it was more being told than being asked. I didn't have much choice. And, the job started the next Monday!

Now understand, Karen was pregnant with our first child, who was scheduled to arrive in this world in a matter of weeks; and while she knew I was in Dallas to look at a potential promotion and move, the idea of taking the position on the spot and agreeing to start in less than a week was not on her radar.

If I were older, I would have passed on the opportunity in Dallas. Putting Karen and our young family through a sudden move at that time in our lives was just too much. But, I was young and afraid, and knowing I needed a job, I said yes and signed the deal before getting on the plane back to Birmingham. It would have been extremely hard for anyone to say no to the corporate guys at a fancy restaurant in those settings. I was going to become the lead, weeknight weather anchor at the CBS affiliate in Dallas.

As usual, that night Karen was gracious and understanding, despite knowing the hardship we were about to endure as her due date approached. Because of the veil of secrecy surrounding the changes at KDFW in Dallas, I was not allowed to tell anyone at Channel 13 in Birmingham I was leaving until my last day, Friday, August 3. So, on Thursday, August 2, I went to work as usual and had to keep my mouth shut about the situation. That was a very unusual day, needless to say, with so many thoughts running through my mind--mostly thoughts of the great memories of the five years I had while calling Channel 13 home.

The announcement was made to the station on Friday afternoon, August 3, near the end of the business day, and before the 5:00 News. At the same time, those losing their jobs in Dallas were being told in private meetings. It was a Times Mirror fruit- basket-turnover kind of day. We announced my departure on the air after the weather segment on the 10:00 news; it was so odd knowing that was the last newscast with Pam Huff, Gene Lively, and Ken Snow all together. A few tears were shed, we said goodbye, and I went home to get ready for what would turn out to be the wildest weekend of my life.

CHAPTER 18
NEW BABY, JOB, AND PLACE TO LIVE

I arrived home after the 10:00 news, and before I even had time to think about the things I needed to do over the weekend in preparedness for that first day in Dallas Monday, it happened. Karen told me "the time has come." She was in labor! We rushed to the hospital, family members gathered together, and the next day, on August 4, 1984, Dr. Paul Perry delivered James Paul Spann into the world. I touched base with Bill Baker in Dallas to let him know, and the station sent some really nice flowers and a kind message of congratulations, but I was STILL expected to be at work in Dallas Monday. Most men these days get a few weeks of family leave; that didn't exist in 1984.

It was a miracle Karen didn't murder me. I mean, her husband was abandoning her two days after childbirth for a job in a strange land far from home. Thankfully, we had plenty of family members to help, but it was still a very challenging situation.

When I hopped on the plane Monday morning, August 6, to fly to Dallas, I was pretty much an emotional wreck. I was leaving my wife and newborn child heading to a new job and a new place we would be calling home. And, to make matters worse, I was told by Baker to get into the weather office and go on the air that first night without talking to the news director (normally my boss). That meant I was walking into the place with no direction, no training, and no idea of how things were done there. And this was a top ten market!

As it turns out, a number of Times Mirror employees were being shipped into Dallas from other markets, and not all of them were there when I arrived. I was one of the first ones in.

The company put me up at a Holiday Inn on Griffin Street, a couple of blocks away from the station in downtown Dallas. After I checked in, I made the quick walk down the street to get into KDFW for the first time. I had to ask directions for the news studio, weather office, the break room, and every other place since it was the first time I was in the building.

As I was told to do, I pretty much kept to myself in the weather office that first day, trying to figure out how the equipment worked, getting a forecast together, and shaking off the remarkable anxiety I was feeling about this whole situation. Some of the news anchors and reporters did come over and introduce themselves, which made me feel a little more at home and not like a weed in the garden of life.

Thankfully the weather in Dallas isn't hard to figure out in August. Hot and dry works most of the time, and that was the case for basically my first four weeks. Lots of days had triple digit heat, and showers were almost impossible to find. The 5:00 news intro billed "Channel 4 News" and "James Spann in the Weather Center". I did my two and a half minutes to the best of my ability, and repeated the performance at 6:00 and 10:00 that night. I doubt if I was very good, but the segments got on the air with graphics.

Thankfully Times Mirror allowed me to fly back home anytime I wanted for that first month, and it was a whirlwind. But clearly Karen had the most difficult time back home with a colicky baby and no sleep. Karen and J.P. finally made it to Dallas; we lived at a Residence Inn until our new home was complete in Plano. And yes, I had to drive the North Central Expressway into work daily; back in the 1980s it was called the North Central *Distressway* because of the excessive volume of traffic and lack of lanes.

The new troops were finally at KDFW by September. The 5:00 news team consisted of news anchors Steve Dawson and Suzanne Moss, sportscaster Paul Crane, and me. For the 6:00 and 10:00 newscasts, Crane and I were joined by news anchors Clarice Tinsley and Steve Bosh. The new news director was none other than Wendell Harris, the same guy that hired me at Birmingham's Channel 13 in 1979.

My job was challenging; we were competing with the legendary WFAA, Channel 8, which in my opinion had the best local news operation in America in the mid-80s. Troy Dungan, the guy with the bow tie, was the main weather anchor and was well liked in the market. But, the true legend was Harold Taft, the "world's greatest weatherman," who was the chief meteorologist at KXAS, Channel 5, the NBC affiliate based in Fort Worth.

CHAPTER 19
MY TIME IN TEXAS

There was no way I could be a factor in the Dallas/Fort Worth TV market unless I gained a grasp of the people, culture, and geography. All of my equity was in Alabama, and I was a stranger in a strange land. With no school visits scheduled, no commercial radio duties, no social media (that didn't come along until 20 years later), and only having to worry about three television weathercasts every weeknight, I decided to spend part of my days driving to learn the market. Some days I would drive four hours, down roads less traveled stopping at any kind of place where people might be gathered together. I introduced myself, asked questions, and did my best to listen and learn. It was a large market, with one county at the time even across the state line in Oklahoma. No way I could visit every town, but I sure tried.

Late in 1984 we installed a Doppler radar unit at Channel 4 down at the transmitter site at Cedar Hill. It was actually designed to be an aircraft radar, and the antenna was a small flat plate with limited distance. I could detect turbulence, as opposed to true radial velocity, but it was new to the market and made an impact. Understand, the WSR 88D National Weather Service Doppler Radar network for the most part was not operational until the 1990s, so this was kind of a big deal at the time.

We actually had very little active weather during my time at Channel 4. Oh sure, we had the occasional ice event and severe weather day, but there were simply no high impact events in the mid-80s there during my tenure.

I did make many new friends in the weather enterprise-- people like Skip Ely and Dave Martin, who were with the National Weather Service in Fort Worth at the time. I first met Al Moller there; I heard him speak a number of times about severe local storms and severe weather preparedness. Al was a storm chaser way before it was cool and a heck of a meteorologist and expert on severe convective storms. I did my best to surround myself with people like Al and soak up the knowledge like a sponge.

In Dallas, I did see an opportunity; it seemed like severe weather coverage was pretty watered-down, and I pitched the idea of going wall-to-wall during tornado warnings. My idea never made any progress; that seemed too outrageous in the mid-1980s, and there was just not that much severe weather at the time.

The working environment at KDFW was somewhat difficult; the news department was unionized (AFTRA), and the engineers had a separate union (IBEW). It seemed like both unions weren't very fond of each other, and I didn't join either one, so I was not the most popular guy in the building. We were never able to catch up with WFAA during my time in Dallas; Channel 8 was dominant in the ratings. And, interestingly enough, those guys would shape how I handled long form severe weather coverage throughout my career.

On August 2, 1985, during the 6:00 news, I was preparing my weather segment, watching radar closely since a few pop-up summer storms were around the metroplex. And, as usual, I had my two meter amateur, handheld radio in the office monitoring the guys on 146.88 MHz, listening for storm reports. Right before my weather segment was to start, I heard multiple, startling reports of a smoke plume coming from the direction of DFW Airport, and talk of some type of incident there.

I went on and did my weather segment about 6:15, and when I was finished I went right back to that two meter radio. From the reports, it was clear a jet had crashed at the big airport. I ran back to the assignment desk to be sure they knew, and from the lukewarm look and rolled eyes, I got the idea they didn't know about it and didn't believe me.

As our sports segment was ending, I saw on a monitor a special report from WFAA, reporting the crash. We completed the newscast without a single mention of the airport situation.

By 6:30 WFAA went into continuous coverage; Channel 4 did its first cut-in about 6:40 and went right back to regular programming. Channel 8's coverage of the crash of Delta Flight 191 that night was second to none. The L-1011 encountered a thunderstorm microburst on approach to DFW; the pilots were unable to escape the violent wind, and the aircraft struck the ground over a mile short of the runway. The crash killed 136 people on board, including 128 of the 152 passengers and 8 of the 11 crew, and the driver of a car on an expressway just north of the airport.

I watched the stellar WFAA wall-wo-wall coverage of this tragedy with extreme interest. My station, KDFW, and the NBC affiliate, KXAS, did watered-down, brief cut-ins during prime time that Friday night, but Channel 8 owned the story. Multiple live shots, live chopper video, accurate and timely information without hyperbole. Anchors were calm. That night on WFAA is running through my veins today when I do continuous tornado coverage.

KDFW in Dallas. Screen grab; newscast was from December 1984.

My plan was to drive back to Alabama after the 10:00 news that night; Karen and J.P. had flown back a few days ago, and we were going to celebrate J.P.'s first birthday together with relatives. Turns out I had to stay on over until Saturday; a "go team" from the FAA wanted to meet with me and review Doppler radar images of the storm I had captured when the crash happened. It was so sad to think about all those that lost their lives that night while we celebrated the first year of life of our son.

Often in Dallas, I would get together with Wendell Harris, the news director, and we would dream up ways of going home. I look back at the brief time in Dallas and still today appreciate the time there, but Karen and I just felt like we were to live our lives in Alabama. Wendell, an Alabama native, also wanted to get home. Working in a big market was never a goal and didn't really appeal to me. I am honestly glad I had the chance to do it at such a young age so I would never have to wonder what it would be like, but deep down I was being called home.

The logic just seemed to suggest I would need to retire from television to make this happen. Making a move back to a smaller market just didn't make sense, and I figured maybe there was something else for me with better, more stable hours. My mind often wandered back to radio; there were some really remarkable stations in the Dallas/Fort Worth market; one of my favorites was KVIL. I loved listening to the station's morning drive guy, Ron Chapman . . . he was full of energy, plugged into the people there, and a ratings giant.

As I approached the end of the two-year contract at Channel 4, my plan to get home involved radio. I got with two old friends, Tom Stipe (longtime producer of the Alabama Crimson Tide Sports Network), and Dave Baird (my long time co-worker in radio and TV), and we started looking for Alabama radio stations to buy. After kicking the tires, we found one that just might work. It was an AM-FM combination in rural West Alabama.

CHAPTER 20
DALLAS TO DEMOPOLIS

The idea of living in a small Alabama town was not foreign to me. Remember, I grew up as a young child in Greenville, about the same size as Demopolis, a beautiful community situated on the banks of the Tombigbee River between Tuscaloosa and Mobile. Karen wasn't too sure about it, but she was getting to a point within one hour of her family in Tuscaloosa and was on board.

Understand, the three of us--Spann, Stipe, and Baird--really didn't have much money, so we had to scrape up the financial resources needed to buy the station in a creative fashion. The asking price was $650,000, which was a pile of money for three very young guys. But, we made it happen, settled on a price, and set closing for June 1986, right when my Dallas contract was up.

Bill Baker at Channel 4 made a very generous offer for me to stay, but going back to Alabama was a done deal for me. Most in Dallas were totally confused . . . why would this guy with such a bright future just walk away from a top ten market and go to a small Alabama town and become obscure. But remember, I was a weather guy in TV, not a TV guy doing weather. There is a huge difference.

Most would have a hard time with the culture shock of moving from Dallas, Texas, to Demopolis, Alabama. Not me--I felt right at home. Soon after taking over the stations there, we changed the call letters of the FM station from WNAN (Nan Jordan was the wife of the first owner) to WZNJ (we kept the "NJ" for Nan Jordan), and the on-air branding was Z-106. The format changed from beautiful music to a hot adult contemporary sound; we were playing songs like "Easy Lover" by Phil Collins and Philip Bailey and "Higher Love" by Steve Winwood.

Yours truly worked morning drive on Z-106. Yep, from lead weather anchor at the CBS affiliate in Dallas, to morning drive radio in Demopolis, Alabama. Call me crazy, but it happened. And, as the owner and manager of a small market radio station, I did so much more than morning drive--lots of sales calls, dreaming up station promotions, and even calling high school football games on Friday nights.

For two years, I was the voice of Demopolis Academy football. And, I must tell you, I had more fun doing that than just about anything else. We did those football broadcasts from the most bizarre places and small towns while on the road; my first road trip was to Canoe, Alabama, on the Florida line, when Demopolis Academy played Escambia Academy. My color guy was Frank Calloway, who also happened to be the minister of music at First Baptist Church of Demopolis.

Most people in town listened to the Demopolis High School football broadcasts over on the AM station, WXAL. High school football was very good for us. It was a profit center, and I always hated it when the season ended.

One good thing about owning a radio station is that you can pretty much do whatever you want. Needless to say, I was the official weather guy for WZNJ and WXAL, and if there was even a strong thunderstorm around, I tested the wall-to-wall coverage idea and found it worked very well with a very positive reception in the community. We didn't have too many high impact weather events during my time in Demopolis, but trust me, when we did, we had continuous coverage on the radio. People really appreciated it.

I spent a year as President of the Demopolis Area Chamber of Commerce, was a member of the Demopolis Rotary Club, and was a deacon at First Baptist Church of Demopolis. I was totally plugged in, but deep down inside I was still feeling the tug to get back into television weather. I was not really a good businessman and I missed the fun of doing weather full time.

At the station, business was good, but it was becoming clear we had borrowed too much money, and the debt service was just too much. We were in the red many months, and by the end of 1988 it was clear the best option was to sell the station, and for me to re-enter the TV weather job market.

In early 1989, there weren't many weather openings that were a good match for me. Not wanting to leave Alabama, I thought the door had closed on my weather career, and it was time to get a real job. But, later that year, something happened in Birmingham that brought the open door I was looking for.

Mike Royer, long-time weather anchor on WBRC, Channel 6, announced in October that he was leaving to go next door to my old station, Channel 13, to start a daily talk show called "Top Of The Morning." I got in touch with Nick Bolton, General Manager of Channel 6, and the next day News Director Steve Minium drove down to Demopolis. We had a long talk sitting on the banks of the Tombigbee River, and we cut the deal on a napkin at the Hardee's on U.S. 80.

CHAPTER 21
BACK TO BIRMINGHAM

After a five-year absence, I returned to Birmingham television as the main weather anchor at WBRC, Channel 6, in November 1989 at the age of 33.

I do believe those five years were important; I made some very important friends in the meteorological community in Dallas and gained confidence knowing I could handle weather in the big time. And, in Demopolis, I had total freedom to experiment with long-form weather coverage without any limitations. And, I learned so much about people, community involvement, and business during the days as a radio station owner. I do believe both were necessary to set the stage for a long-term, successful career in television back home in Birmingham.

The evening WBRC anchor team in November 1989 consisted of Scott Richards and Janet Hall, sportscaster Rick Karle, and weather anchor James Spann.

My first month at Channel 6 did indeed feature a high impact weather event just north of our market. On November 15, 1989, a number of severe weather parameters were in place, and we were watching radar developments closely. During the afternoon, a small tornado touched down near the community of Mellow Valley, in Clay County, but otherwise the day was relatively quiet.

Then, a squall line entered Northwest Alabama about 3:00 p.m., and at that point it looked like the primary issue during the afternoon and evening hours was going to be straight line winds along the line. About 4:20, an isolated cell merged with the squall line over the southwest part of Huntsville, near Redstone Arsenal, and within minutes an EF-4 tornado dropped from the sky, moving through the southern part of Huntsville.

It destroyed or damaged 80 businesses, 3 churches, a dozen apartment buildings, and more than 1,000 cars. It moved on, climbing over Garth Mountain, demolishing Jones Valley Elementary School, and destroying 259 homes in the Jones Valley area. In all, the tornado killed 21 people and injured 463 others. Unfortunately, there was no tornado warning until several minutes after the twister touched down . . . this was before Doppler Radar was in operational use in Alabama.

It was rather amazing to watch these developments unfold from our Birmingham weather office on Red Mountain; that night we were able to pick up live coverage on WAAY-TV, which remained on the air throughout the event thanks to a generator. The following day, I went to Huntsville, where I did the weather live during the midday news in the midst of a snow squall. That was surreal; I could barely see across the street due to the heavy snow, which put a white blanket on the rubble of the buildings and cars destroyed by the tornado. During the 5:00 and 6:00 newscasts that evening, live from Huntsville, the wind chill index hovered near 5 degrees. One of our camera guys passed out during the 6:00 news;

to this day I really don't know if it was from exhaustion or the severe cold.

The next month, December 1989, featured a very impressive cold wave. Dramatic predictions of intense cold diving all the way to the Gulf Coast dominated the headlines during the middle part of the month. On the morning of Tuesday, December 21, a powerful 1052 millibar high was over southern Saskatchewan. At Swift Current, the thermometer read -39F and the barometer 1053.2 millibars. Arctic air was plunging south behind a cold front that was pushing through Memphis. In Birmingham, it was 42 and .in Memphis, it was 19. By the morning of the 22nd, the mercury stood at 15 degrees in Birmingham. It never got any higher that day. By midnight, the mercury would be down to 4. It was -3 in Memphis and -10 in Nashville that cold morning.

For Birmingham, the coldest morning would be the 23rd, when the mercury dropped to 1 degree. Along the Gulf Coast, it was an amazing 7 in Houston, 11 in Lake Charles, 11 in New Orleans and 10 in Pensacola. A total of 122 cities across the central and eastern United States reported record low temperatures for December 23rd.

The week after Christmas brought a snow/ice scare, requiring me to stay up through the night. This turned out to be much ado about nothing, but we have to have a warm body in the weather office anyway. I think I actually dozed off about 4:15 a.m. in the quietness of the studio and weather office, but all of a sudden it sounded like an army was marching into the place, and I was absolutely startled. Through my sleepy eyes, I saw person after person entering the other side of the studio, and before I could gather my thoughts, a cowbell started ringing. Then, a voice said, "James Spann, the world's greatest weatherman. . .come on over and tell us what's going on."

Through my bewilderment, I realized the voice was none other than Country Boy Eddie (CBE). He did an early morning, local country music show on WBRC for 37 years; I watched him every morning in Tuscaloosa before going to school. I simply forgot I was now at Channel 6, and on the same crew as CBE That was the first of many pre-dawn appearances on the Country Boy Eddie show over the years. One thing I learned about Eddie--the man doesn't have a stressed bone in his body. And, he was a very successful businessman. He bought the time from Channel 6 and sold his own ads. Just about everything on the show was a paid advertisement except for some of the singers.

CHAPTER 22
THE NEXT LEVEL

February 1990 was an active month for tornadoes in Alabama. On Saturday, February 7, smaller tornadoes touched down in the broad area from Birmingham to Tuscaloosa. I was back in Demopolis that morning but made the quick trip back to work with weekend weather anchor Jonathan Elias handling the event.

Then, late Friday night, February 9 into the pre-dawn hours Saturday February 10, another severe weather set-up resulted in an EF-1 tornado that moved through the highly populated Shelby County communities of Pelham and Helena. Since this was an after midnight tornado and we didn't have any really significant programming, I decided to try, for the first time, wall-to-wall coverage. I stayed on the air for about one hour (which was an eternity for weather coverage at the time) during the entire event, hoping management wouldn't get upset.

Turned out to be good decision; I was shocked at the dozens and dozens of letters we received, complimentary of our coverage. And, we owned the story since Channel 13 just did the usual short cut-in type coverage. I encouraged management to consider letting me go wall-to-wall during tornado warnings at any hour of the day and night, but they weren't ready for that.

After the big events of November 1989 and February 1990, I knew I had to up my game in many ways. One was getting a formal education in meteorology. In order for my career to really take off, that had to happen.

Thankfully, Mississippi State University (MSU) had just started offering their geoscience and meteorology classes via distance learning. MSU is just two hours west of Birmingham, and I could easily make the drive over any time that needed to happen.

I am so thankful for Dr. Mark Binkley, the first director of the program, and the team at Mississippi State for the opportunity. My local proctor for exams was my mentor, J.B. Elliott, who had just retired from his position with the National Weather Service in Birmingham. J.B. and his wife, Judy, would always be so hospitable to me when I took an exam at their home on Winola Lane in Huffman. I completed the program and got the certificate from MSU in August 1992. That opened the door for me to earn the "Seal of Approval" from the American Meteorological Society (AMS), and the National Weather Association.

Later, the AMS developed the Certified Broadcast Meteorologist program (CBM). To earn the CBM, broadcasters must hold a degree in meteorology or the equivalent from an accredited college or university, pass a rigorous written examination, and have their on-air work reviewed to assess technical competence, informational value, explanatory value, and communication skills. I was the 33rd meteorologist in the nation to earn one of these; I would have liked to have been in the first ten, but I was so busy those days that it was just hard finding the time to take the written exam.

During those days, I learned much about television, perhaps more than at any other time in my career, thanks to the remarkable news professionals I worked with, people like News Director Steve Minium, and producers Elbert Tucker and Bob Clinkingbeard. These were big time professionals that understood television news and production, and their influence on me is still appreciated. Channel 6 News was well done, well produced, and well watched. We were the number one news station in the market by far. I loved working with Scott, Janet, and Rick on the air, and we all got along and worked well together. That can't be said for every anchor team on TV.

CHAPTER 23
THE BLIZZARD OF 1993

For most of the country, with the exception of the Pacific Coast and the Desert Southwest, people say the same thing, but think the phrase is unique to their part of the nation: "If you don't like the weather around here, wait a few minutes, and it will change." And, most think the weather where they live is especially hard to forecast.

The truth is that putting out an accurate weather forecast is a challenge just about everywhere. Different parts of the nation have unique circumstances that stand out to those in operational meteorology. In Alabama, the two biggest challenges are forecasting timing and placement of thunderstorms on summer afternoons and winter storms in the cold season.

Just about every afternoon during June, July, and August thunderstorms form across Alabama with a buoyant atmosphere loaded with moisture. But, those storms tend to form in totally random locations, and there is no way we can tell people at 7:00 in the morning where storms will be located at 3:00 or 4:00 that afternoon. Accordingly, the forecast just about every day in summer says, "partly sunny, hot, and humid with scattered, mostly afternoon and evening showers and thunderstorms." That forecast doesn't help anyone trying to plan a picnic or outdoor event at a certain time. I am hoping the next generations of meteorologists make some progress with air mass thunderstorms across the Deep South in summer, but I am not getting my hopes up.

Winter storms in Alabama are certain to cause weeping and gnashing of teeth, especially in the weather office. They don't happen often, our skill set in dealing with them is low, and people often have selective hearing when it comes to winter storm forecasts. Some prefer to get winter storm information from others in the checkout line at the grocery store, in the car line at the elementary school, or from Uncle Ted, who once took a weather class when he was in college 30 years ago.

I still have horrible memories of the January 1982 ice storm bust, and they were even fresher in my mind in the early 1990s at Channel 6. But I hadn't dealt with too many really significant weather issues since that storm in 1982; after all this is Alabama, a low latitude state with infrequent snow and ice encounters.

The weather team at Channel 6 in March 1993 was a really good one. I handled weeknights, Dan Satterfield did mornings and Kevin Selle (who was known to the world back then as Kevin Collins) was on the air weekends. I considered my long mentor J.B. Elliott also a part of the team, although he worked for The Weather Company, a private weather business we started in 1991. Once J.B. retired from the National Weather Service, we wanted him on our side. One of the first products from The Weather Company was a fax product with detailed weather information sent to businesses that needed serious weather information. Smartphones and the Internet as we know it today didn't exist back then; if you wanted to get on line, you used CompuServe or Prodigy with dial up modems.

John Oldshue, a former intern with us, was another founding partner of The Weather Company along with Bill Murray and David Black. David had done weekend weather with me at Channel 13 back in the early 80s.

On Wednesday, March 10, Kevin was in the weather office with me as the new Limited Fine Mesh (LFM) and the Medium Range Forecast (MRF) model maps arrived over DIFAX. Back in the early 1990s, we received maps and graphics from the National Weather Service via one of these machines, which printed the low-resolution maps on moist paper. Once the maps were dry, they were hung up on a wall or spread out across large desks so we could see multiple graphics at the same time. I should mention that they smelled really funky, too.

The MRF that day put an intense surface low just below Pensacola (way under 1000 millibars) by Friday night and Saturday (March 12-13), with colder, Arctic air flooding into Alabama: a perfect combination for a snow storm. Kevin and I just looked at each other, wondering who would be the first to say it. Who had the guts to forecast a big snow storm in the middle of March in Alabama?

Earlier runs at the MRF had hinted at this possibility, so model consistency was good. In 1993 there were no weather blogs, no apps, no social media. It was pretty much television exclusively when it came to mass distribution of weather information. So, I made the decision to be bold and forecast a chance of snow for the first part of the weekend on Channel 6 News at 5:00. I could almost hear giggles from the audience.

The next night, Thursday, March 11, the LFM (now within range of the event) supported the MRF idea, and with each run the system looked more dynamic, with lower pressure and colder air. I made the decision to mention the potential for over 3 inches of snow and impact on travel and life in general on the early evening news. And, by 10:00 that Thursday night, I started mentioning the possibility of over 5 inches of snow in spots. Of course, I did my best to communicate uncertainty in that forecast, giving me some kind of out if that turned out to be a bust.

Early Friday morning, March 12 models and the pattern continued to favor a major Southern snowstorm, and with a 980 mb low expected to be in the northern Gulf of Mexico within 24 hours, that could indeed bring blizzard conditions to parts of North and Central Alabama. During the day, I used "4 to 10" inches for Birmingham, Tuscaloosa, Anniston, and Gadsden and did my best with commercial radio (I was on Magic 96 FM and WERC AM in Birmingham in 1993) and the weather fax to warn people. Dan Satterfield was on Channel 6 on the morning shift with the same message.

We highlighted the chance of major power outages, and potential for this to be one of the strongest winter storms on record for the eastern third of the U.S. Nice thing about technology these days is that anyone can go on YouTube and watch these old weathercasts. We really tried to get the word out. But, in mid-March, many just didn't listen or believe us.

Snow increased rapidly in intensity after dark that Friday night, March 12, and it pretty much snowed all night. As the surface low to the south intensified, winds gusted to hurricane force at our studio atop Red Mountain, resulting in a *whiteout* after midnight. Photographer Bill Castle, who was sent out to shoot video of a business whose building collapsed due to the weight of the snow, was disoriented on the way back due to zero visibility. Crews in the field were told to get back to the station if possible simply to protect their lives. That was no ordinary Alabama snow storm.

Perhaps the most memorable part of the blizzard was thundersnow or convective snow bands that brought lightning and thunder. It was surreal from the back door as we looked over the city of Birmingham from Red Mountain.

During the night I had the pleasure of working in the warm studio; Kevin was the guy positioned out the back door in the raging blizzard for live reports. The hat worn by Kevin has become legendary in the weather enterprise over the years; I still have it in my office.

The blizzard started to wind down about sunrise Saturday, March 13. As the sun came up, it was a winter wonderland as we looked out from atop Red Mountain. Birmingham's official snow total was 13 inches, based on data from the airport, but some of the southern suburbs had almost two feet. Snow drifts on the mountain were high over parked cars. All 67 Alabama counties had measurable snow; it was our new snowstorm of record.

But there was little time to celebrate the beauty. Almost a quarter of a million people in the state had no power, countless people were stranded on roads and highways, and temperatures would drop into the single digits the next morning--Birmingham's low on Sunday March 14 was 2 degrees. The state was shut down, and there were so many critical needs. I spent the weekend on Channel 6 and local radio trying to get people with services connected with the people with needs. And again, this was before smartphones and social media. I think my best memories involved doing radio on WERC with Tommy Charles. With so many people without power, the commercial radio stations were worth their weight in gold that weekend.

I did try to dig my car out of a snow drift Sunday morning. We were living in an apartment in Hoover while a new house was being built, and Karen and J.P. had no power. I figured I could dig the car out and go check on them for an hour or so. But, this Southern boy learned quickly that day why so many people have a heart attack shoveling show. After 30 minutes, it seemed like I made no progress at all, and I just gave up.

The power outage at the apartment would go on to last about one week. We wound up moving into the Wynfrey Hotel at the Riverchase Galleria for a few days.

Perhaps the most interesting moment that weekend came Sunday night. I got a call from none other than Country Boy Eddie. For the first time in 37 years he was snowed in and could not get to work, and he asked me to host his program the next morning. I went downstairs and woke up long time newsman Bill Bolen, who was sleeping on a cot, and told him I was not doing the "CBE" show by myself; he had to help out.

I do believe that turned out to be the worst hour of local television ever in the Birmingham market. It was brutal. Thankfully we had some country music videos to play, but having to read commercials for products like rabbit nuggets and jogging in a Jug was a little too much. I didn't know whether to laugh or cry. I am so thankful that, to my knowledge, the video of that one particular Country Boy Eddie show doesn't exist on YouTube or in any other place.

We rang Eddie's cowbell every time the temperature climbed one degree, and we all celebrated when we went above 32 degrees about 8:00 that morning. Life got back to normal by afternoon as the historic March snow melted away. It was a Southern snowstorm for the ages.

CHAPTER 24
LIFE AWAY FROM TELEVISION

Occasionally I see young people indicate on resumes that they "live, sleep, and eat weather." Now that is just too weird. I understand they are trying to communicate the fact that they have a passion for the science of meteorology, but I would prefer to hire those who are well rounded in life. I was working for Channel 6 in my 30s, what some would call the "prime of life." Unfortunately, TV culture can be pretty harsh, easily leading one down the wrong path toward selfishness and narcissism.

Like many TV people, I thought a little too much of myself and was pretty self-centered. Understand, I looked good on paper; I was involved in a number of ministries, taught Sunday School at a large church, and did school talks on a regular basis. But, how people look on paper doesn't necessarily reflect the state of their hearts.

Being self-centered can easily lead to frustration, bitterness, and anger. I was blessed with a supportive wife and family; our marriage, while far from perfect, was strong after 10 years, and J.P. was in elementary school and doing well. I also had a good church home, and some friends there knew my internal struggle--the classic battle we all face between being self-centered and God-centered. Time is spent worrying about self or about helping other people.

After encouraging me to pray a simple prayer about opening my eyes to the needs of those around me, I gave it a shot. Funny how one short prayer can change a life.

The next day I woke up with a certain person on my mind and in my heart. I had to figure this was a person with a need I was to meet, but oddly enough, it was a person I really didn't want to help. It was my father.

Understand, he left when I was 7 years old and he came to my mind strongly at the age of 37 ... almost thirty years to the day. When my father left, he pretty much crushed me like a bug on a windshield. The pain never went away; it faded but is there to this day. This was the one person in the world I was to help? I didn't really know if he was alive or dead, where he lived, or anything else about the guy. He wasn't exactly on our Christmas card list.

As you might expect, I found out he was indeed alive. And, for that entire thirty-year period he had lived in Alabama. I had no idea. And, I learned I had a half-brother, about 10 years younger than I was. Again, this was all news to me.

I committed a Saturday to finding him. I was told he lived in a suburb of Huntsville, the place where I was born. I made the two-hour drive with a friend, and after knocking on some doors, it happened. The door opened, and I was looking into the eyes of my father for the first time in thirty years. It is very hard to explain what happened at that moment, but right away some things were taken away from me--things that needed to go: hate, anger, and rage just went away.

You see, I was a hothead at that time in my life. It was very easy for me to fly off the handle without much prompting, and that is a characteristic nobody needs or wants. I have plenty of weaknesses in life, but after that encounter with my father, I was a changed man. God's greatest miracles are changed lives, and I am one of them. You can pretty much punch me in the nose, and I will just smile back.

And, while anger was taken away, some sweet memories drifted back into my mind. Things we did together before he left. My father took me fishing many times in South Butler County near Georgiana. He took me to the Ringling Brothers Barnum and Bailey Circus at Garrett Coliseum in Montgomery. It was as if these things happened just weeks ago. The memories were rich and clear. Maybe my father did love me. I cherish these memories to this day. Nobody can steal them from me.

I believed I was there that day to share my Christian faith with my father. I told him that he shared my problem in that only perfect people go to heaven, according to the Bible. And, that God's solution, determined before eternity, was for Him to send His one Son to live a perfect life here and make the sacrifice for us. I told him that he simply had to accept that gift like a child accepts a gift at a birthday party.

And, I told my father that if he was the only person on the planet, God loved him so much that Jesus Christ could come and die just for him. Pretty powerful stuff.

Unfortunately, my father didn't accept what I had to say. He couldn't. You see, my father was drunk. I learned that day that my father was an alcoholic. Quite frankly, the smell of alcohol on his breath was another childhood memory that came back to me that day. He had a condition known as alcohol dementia, caused by long-term, excessive consumption of booze, resulting in neurological damage and impaired cognitive function. I honestly don't think he knew it was me. The conversation was pretty much like I was talking to a brick wall.

Quite frankly, my father's behavior that day was embarrassing. He urinated in his front yard where our encounter took place, and used language that would even be out of place in a TV newsroom. Vulgar profanity.

But, even if he could not understand me, I told him that day he was forgiven. And, I meant it. I told him that God had forgiven me for my sin, and the least I could do was to forgive him. Honestly, I think that was the point of the encounter that day. It wasn't about helping my father, but it was about me being helped by that statement of forgiveness.

I love the movie "Field of Dreams." At the end, a middle-aged man gets to somehow go back in time and have a catch with his father. I weep openly every time I watch it. You see, my dream was to have a catch with my dad. For me, that dream did not happen. I did my best to develop a relationship with him on other visits, but his condition simply wouldn't allow it. He died the next year in a government facility in Tennessee. Nobody in the family wanted anything to do with him, and I would ultimately take him home, back to Butler County. I split the cost of having him cremated with my half-brother, and I sprinkled the ashes on the family gravesite in Industry, a small community not far from where my father took me fishing as a young child.

CHAPTER 25
CHANGING CHANNELS

The local television business went through a huge transformation in the mid-1990s. Ownership changes and consolidations meant a radically different landscape. At Channel 6, we had four different owners in three years. Keeping up with it all was dizzying; I almost lost count of the 401K retirement accounts I had with the different owners. The fourth owner would turn out to be News Corporation, the owner of the Fox Television Network, which at the time was still the new kid on the block taking on the legacy networks (ABC, CBS, and NBC). It was announced that Channel 6, a long-time ABC affiliate, was going to change affiliation to the Fox network in the fall of 1996.

That left ABC scrambling to find a new affiliate for the Birmingham market, and the company ultimately decided to give it to Allbritton Communications, which operated a series of other ABC affiliates around the nation, including WJLA-TV in Washington, DC. The problem for Allbritton was that there was no Birmingham TV station available to them, so in a creative way, they gained possession of smaller UHF stations in nearby Tuscaloosa and Anniston. One of them was WCFT-TV, Channel 33, where my TV career started back in the late 1970s in Tuscaloosa. The Anniston station was WJSU-TV, Channel 40.

Their plan was to build a large, consolidated operation in Birmingham, combining the staffs from the two stations and hiring new people to build a brand new operation to compete in the larger market. New transmitter facilities were constructed for Channels 33 and 40 so the over-the-air signal could penetrate the city of Birmingham. Allbritton decided to brand the new station "ABC 33/40," and the studio would be built in Hoover, a large suburb of Birmingham about 10 miles south of the city center.

On the surface, the odds of this working sure seemed like a long shot. Trying to compete with the legendary Birmingham stations would be hard enough, but the new ABC 33/40 would not even have a city grade signal over much of Birmingham.

The head of Allbritton was Joe L. Allbritton, but his son, Robert, was to be the one in charge of building his unique station in Alabama. Knowing this was a challenging situation, Allbritton plan was to conduct a talent raid in the market, hiring away established on-air personalities for the new station to give it instant credibility.

Needless to say, I was watching developments with great interest and was seeing a number of my associates at Channel 6 turning in their resignations for a job at the new ABC affiliate in the market in the summer of 1996. Ultimately, I would be contacted by the Allbritton operation, and we met on a number of occasions. On the surface, it sure seemed like there wasn't much of a chance for the new kids on the block. But, I was intrigued by the family ownership and the vision shared by Robert Allbritton.

After much deliberation and prayer, I made the decision to change channels. I would seriously miss all my friends and associates at WBRC, but I felt Allbritton's operation would be a much better fit for me and my family going forward for many reasons. Perhaps most importantly, I was given the green light to go wall-to-wall during a tornado warning for any county in the market. I had dreamed of this for years and it was coming true.

Understand, however, this was a huge gamble. I put my career on the line; if the new station failed, I might have to pack up and find another job somewhere else. The odds of failure were pretty high with the two small UHF signals in an ocean of VHF powerhouse stations.

One positive thing was that the size of the Birmingham TV market jumped significantly because of all of this. Tuscaloosa and Anniston, which had been separate markets, were rolled into the Birmingham market, making it the 40th largest in the nation at the time.

So, I left WBRC on the last day of August 1996. The next day, September 1, ABC 33/40 signed on the air from its new facility in Riverchase. But, due to some legal maneuvering, I would not join the new station until October 1. Bob Baron, long-time meteorologist in Huntsville and the founder of Baron Services, handled weather that first month while I was on the sideline.

The month of September 1996 was very unusual for me. I pretty much felt unemployed and technically, that was my status. I was no longer with Channel 6 and was yet to be on the payroll at ABC 33/40. The deal with the new station was in theory a secret, and I wasn't able to say much other than I was just "taking some time away" from television.

But, on Tuesday, October 1, I reported to work at Birmingham's new ABC affiliate. The James Spann move was kept under cover, and nobody in the building except a selected few, knew I was a new employee and on the air that evening. But, after my first newscast at 5:00, it was a secret no more. The 5:00 anchor team that day consisted of news anchors Dave Baird and Linda Mays, meteorologist James Spann, and sports anchor Mike Raita. I was delighted to be with Dave again; we had worked together for Bert Bank back in the 1970s, playing rock and roll music on the radio during our youth. Linda and Mike both came over from WBRC with me.

Mike and I were on the 6:00 and 10:00 team with Brenda Ladun, another journalist that made the move from Channel 6, and John Thomas, who came down from Baltimore.

The early newscasts on ABC 33/40 were amazingly smooth for a station that really wasn't ready to go on the air. The complete infrastructure wasn't really finished until sometime in 1997; that is when our live radar atop Double Oak Mountain was installed, and the microwave system was completed. Those installations allowed us to go live.

The first chance in my career to go wall-to-wall with tornado coverage came on January 24, 1997, when an EF-2 moved through the eastern section of Tuscaloosa. Just before 5 p.m., a tornado touched down south of

I-59 and west of Alabama Highway 69. The tornado moved northeastward, passing near the intersection of Skyland and McFarland Boulevards. A Books-a-Million and a Gayfers suffered damage to their roofs at McFarland Mall. The twister crossed the interstate and intensified. Several homes were damaged in the Woodland Hills neighborhood. A 71-year-old retired physician was killed when a tree limb was propelled into the windshield of his pick-up truck. It was the first tornado fatality of the year in the U.S.

The tornado roared northeastward toward Five Points East. The manager of the Food World store saw the approaching tornado and ushered shoppers into the store. The tornado tossed cars like toys. One was blown through the roof of the grocery store.

We were on the air non-stop for almost two hours, and I will never forget what happened after the coverage stopped. Literally the entire staff of the TV station came into the studio and gave the weather team a standing round of applause. I sure didn't feel like we deserved that, but it was a great example of the camaraderie we had in those early days. After all those years of being restricted with short cut-ins, I had the freedom to go on the air and stay on the air when any county in our market went under a tornado warning. It was our policy and our promise. And, that promise would define this new television station the next year.

CHAPTER 26
APRIL 8, 1998

In the spring of 1998, I was 41 years old, and about a year and a half into the new position at ABC 33/40, where we were "building our station around you." Life was pretty hectic; our second child, Ryan, came along in August of 1997, 13 years after J.P. was born in August 1984. Yes, God has a sense of humor.

So, we were back to diapers and sleepless nights, while trying to help the older get settled into middle school. Unfortunately for J.P., he became the built-in babysitter at the house. Thankfully, he was always willing to lend a helping hand to watch his younger brother.

Away from the station, I was involved in a ministry that was in the process of buying a commercial FM radio station for over 10 million dollars; this would become "Reality 101," serving the northern half of Alabama with contemporary Christian music. The studios were built in Brookwood Mall, and we hired my old boss, Wendell Harris, to run the station.

On top of everything else, we were building a private weather business called "The Weather Company." This was home to my radio weather services and other products and services for industry and consumers. I also did weather on over two dozen radio stations around the nation, To run the business we hired Bill Hardekopf away from the Birmingham Barons, a Chicago White Sox AA minor league team in town. Bill loved baseball and professional sports, but he was rarely home during the long baseball season and didn't want his kids growing up without him. It was a perfect fit for both of us. In a few years, Bill would also take over the General Manager position at Reality 101.

I should mention "The Weather Company" is now "The Weather Factory"; we sold the name to the Weather Channel, which in turn sold that part of their business (the digital side) to IBM in 2016.

April 8, 1998, was a typical busy day. I had a Reality 101 meeting that morning with my friend and local attorney Dale Wallace, who also served on the radio station board of directors. Like most mornings with a severe weather risk, I was very preoccupied with what might happen later that day and left the meeting early to get to the weather office at ABC 33/40.

You see, it was one of those rare "high risk" days . . . the highest level of severe weather risk defined by the Storm Prediction Center. This appears only a few days each year, and it simply means that all parameters are in place for a significant severe weather event, including potential for especially violent, long-track tornadoes.

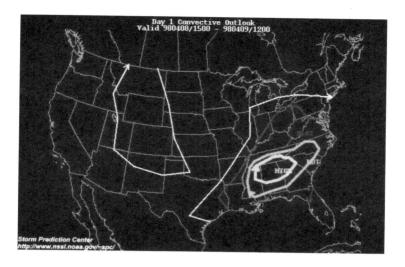

The afternoon was eerily quiet, but we all knew the atmosphere was a powder keg with a remarkable combination of instability (the ability of air parcels to rise freely), and shear (a change of wind direction and/or speed, with height). It was the usual case of nervously waiting and watching in the ABC 33/40 Weather Center that afternoon. Mark Prater was with me at the station; John Oldshue was out in the field in our new storm spotter van. Our new radar atop Double Oak Mountain was oddly devoid of any significant echoes.

Later that evening, it started quickly. Storms developed rapidly as our 6:00 news was ending, and the first tornado warning of the day was issued for Pickens and Tuscaloosa Counties in West Alabama shortly before 7:00. As per our new policy, we went on the air and stayed on the air. I had no idea what was on ABC's prime time schedule that night, and quite frankly, I really didn't care. We had work to do.

A tornado touched down in Pickens County with that first storm and stayed on the ground for 17 miles into Tuscaloosa County. Even though he tornado passed north of the cities of Tuscaloosa and Northport, it did cause some very significant damage and was rated EF-3. We had to pay attention to churches in the path because this was a Wednesday night, and many Alabamians attend mid-week services that usually run from 7:00 to 8:00.

That same supercell thunderstorm dropped a second tornado, this one in northeast Tuscaloosa County, and it became a monster that went on to define ABC 33/40 and my career at the time. The radar signature still haunts me to this day; some in the weather business called it the "mother of all hooks." A hook echo on the right rear flank of a supercell often represents a tornado. And, at the tail end of the hook was the dreaded debris ball. a small area of higher reflectivity caused by the radar beam bouncing off objects lofted up in the tornado, like trees, boards, bricks, hails, parts of homes, and furniture.

This large, wedge tornado, later rated EF-5, the highest intensity on the Enhanced Fujia scale, tore through communities like Oak Grove, Rock Creek, Sylvan Springs, McDonald Chapel, Edgewater, and Pratt City, all in the western part of the Birmingham metropolitan area. It was on the ground for 30 miles and lifted just northwest of downtown Birmingham.

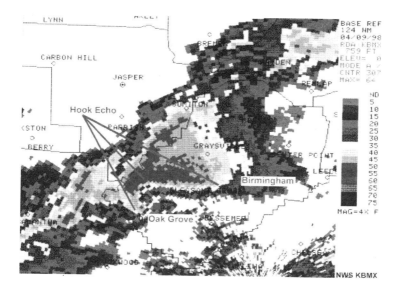

Most of the damage came after the sun was down. This storm occurred 9 years before the iPhone was launched, so to this day we have no photographs or video of the tornado. There was a remarkable moment during our live coverage; at the time we had a SKYCAM atop the western part of Red Mountain on a tower we owned, overlooking the western suburbs. While you couldn't see the tornado, you could see the power grid going down systematically across that part of Jefferson County.

We were tuned to the 146.88 MHz repeater in the weather office, listening to amateur radio spotters in the field, and the first reports didn't sound good. There was talk of "complete destruction" at Oak Grove School, and the need for as many ambulances as possible. John Oldshue was on the scene in Edgewater within minutes of the tornado's passage, and his report was chilling--massive damage, many injured and missing. Total chaos. Our chief photographer, Bill Castle, had live shots up immediately, and his television lights shooting through the eerie darkness revealed much human suffering and neighborhoods that were wiped off the map.

But, we had to keep focused; that same supercell storm dropped yet another tornado. . .this one east of Birmingham. It would touch down along U.S. 411 at Bethel Baptist Church, which was destroyed, passing over Bald Rock Mountain, within a mile or two of our Channel 40 transmitter tower, and then down north of Pell City into the Wattsville, a community in St. Clair County. That one was rated EF-2.

The priority in TV weather coverage must be on protecting human life. While there was much to report in the western suburbs of Birmingham, where an EF-5 had just touched down, taking care of the people in danger in St. Clair County was more important. There were far too many television stations in the country that broke away and went wall-to-wall on the damage in the city, ignoring the people still in danger in rural areas to the east. That was wrong and inexcusable.

That big, nasty supercell moved into Georgia about 11:00, and we then turned it over to news, which went into continuous coverage of the catastrophic damage in the western part of Birmingham. The live video was riveting and heartbreaking at the same time.

About midnight, the news director, Garry Kelly, ran into the weather office for a brief moment, asking me to man our helicopter at the first light of day to fly over the damage since I knew the territory better than anyone else. He also mentioned briefly that we were the only local station on the air with wall-to-wall coverage of the event that night. I didn't have time to think about it then, but later I realized that night could change everything about the way all local stations covered severe weather in this market. We owned the story that night, and people noticed. Along with, of course, with every other station in town.

CHAPTER 27
TROLLS, HATERS, AND KNOW-IT-ALLS

It was well past midnight, and the chopper was to leave the helipad at the station at 5:30am. My heart was still beating out of my chest after the tornado coverage and I knew I needed to calm down and get a short nap before another big day. It was at that time I made a big mistake; I saw the voicemail light flashing on my phone, and I thought it might be wise to check those messages.

Why was that a mistake? It became very clear as I listened to the first message. It was an older lady who sounded like she might be in her 70s. And, she wasn't happy. That woman lit into me for "cutting off her story." You see, we started doing weather cut-ins every thirty minutes at 2:00 that afternoon, and there happened to be a program on ABC at that hour called "General Hospital." I have lived in Alabama long enough to know what it means when an older lady tells me about her *story* . . . those are her words for soap opera. Understand, the cut-ins were only 3 to 5 minutes, but that didn't really matter. That woman chewed me out in the most colorful language. I have been around foul-mouthed news people for a long time, but even some of the words used in that voice mail message were new to me. And, I don't think I have heard a lady that old use the F bomb before. From there she started talking ugly about my mom. Now that was when she crossed the line.

I hung up the phone, and that was the last time I have used the hard-wired phone in my office. I am proud to say today that I don't know my work number, don't know how to get voicemail anymore, and don't even know where my station phone is located. You see, email was becoming pretty mainstream in 1998, and I decided that if people needed me, that was the exclusive way to get in touch with me after that night. That lady ended my station phone use.

That is just one example of dealing with what I call "trolls, haters, and know-it-alls," or "THK" for short. I would classify the lady on the voice mail a hater based on her nasty language and personal attacks. Trolls are negative nellies looking for a fight. They pick on you, criticize you, and try to exploit any mistake or weakness. True keyboard warriors that are actually cowards, they tend to run when you stand up to them. And, the know-it-alls are mental giants (in their minds) that know more about everything than you do. They know EVERYTHING about applied meteorology, climatology, thunderstorms, tornadoes, hurricanes, blizzards, and every other kind of weather event. And, we are all idiots compared to them--an odd form of narcissism.

In the early days, the THK crowd had to use phone calls or snail mail. But, as early as the Compuserve and Prodigy days, they discovered a whole world to spread their vitriol. Today, I deal with these guys on a daily basis. I had to cut off an NBA basketball game on Christmas Day in 2015 that featured Golden State and Cleveland--Lebron vs Curry. A supercell dropped an EF-2 tornado in the southwest part of the city of Birmingham. Many could have been killed, but the warning process worked well, and there was no loss of life and few injuries.

Within a few minutes of having to cut off that game, I saw the first email rolling in, and it said, "You should have been aborted by a coat hanger." Classic example of a hater.

I get THK messages now across all social media platforms: Facebook, Twitter, Instagram, Snapchat, etc. You name it, they use it. I often say those people can't hurt my feelings because I don't have any feelings left after doing this for so long. And, I have gotten to be pretty proficient in dealing with them. My position is, if you dish it out, you have to be able to take it.

During each severe weather event, I take one choice message from a troll, hater, or know-it-all, and either retweet the hate (if it comes in on Twitter), or do a screen grab on other platforms and send it out for the world to see. Sure, we have plenty of those that don't like us doing wall-to-wall tornado coverage, but we also have lots of supporters. Trust me; the haters don't know what to do when a large crowd stands up against them. They usually run away like roaches.

Dealing with the public involves a strange combination of grace and sass. And, in this business, we had better have skin thicker than leather.

I should also point out that we have to understand the difference between hate and constructive criticism. There is a huge difference, and we have to be able to recognize the messages that are critical, but useful. That is the only way we can get better. I have an email folder called "hate mail," but it is actually mostly from people offering suggestions on how to get better. They sign them with their names, and I am thankful for all of them. I cruise over to that folder often.

I honestly think the know-it-alls might be the most problematic. Not only do they get on our nerves, but they have learned how to gain fans by throwing out wild forecasts 2, 3, and 4 weeks in advance of extreme weather events that in most cases never happen.

They usually begin as harmless weather enthusiasts who start a social media account, usually a Facebook page. Let me stress that there is absolutely nothing wrong with that. In fact, I think it is a wonderful opportunity for young people who love weather. However, the problem begins when they learn the secret of getting likes and followers by forecasting outrageous, high impact weather events weeks in advance; snow storms in winter; tornadoes in spring; and hurricanes in summer.

The classic know-it-all sits behind the computer screen, looking for that magical model map in the 10-15 day range (or even at longer ranges) that paints the doomsday scenario. They have absolutely no knowledge of the physics, limitations, or biases of Numerical Weather Prediction (NWP) and refuse to even consider ensemble output (a set of forecasts that present the range of future weather possibilities based on multiple simulations, each with a slight variation of its initial conditions).

When they post that one deterministic model map with the major, potentially life-threatening snowstorm 2 weeks out, their eyes light up because of all the likes, shares, and engagement. It is a rush of happiness and contentment thanks to dopamine, a neurochemical known as the "reward molecule" that's released after certain human actions or behaviors.

Of course, there is absolutely no skill in a specific forecast of a high impact event like a snow storm 2 to 3 weeks in advance. Pattern recognition, yes. Specifics? No. But it doesn't matter. Those wild model maps will get shared hundreds, and in most cases thousands, of times. Oddly enough, when the event never happens, people tend to remain loyal to the know-it-alls despite no accuracy or accountability. And, over a period of time, they can build a huge, loyal group of followers.

I have learned those loyal followers tend to see professional meteorologists as their enemy. On September 5, 2018, as Hurricane Florence was getting stronger over the Atlantic, I posted the following information on Twitter as the know-it-alls were posting wild model maps and forecasting a landfall point (and intensity) ten days out:

A friendly reminder: posting deterministic model output with tropical cyclone positions 10 days out to get shares and likes (or to scare people) isn't cool. It serves no good purpose. A drunk donkey could pull this data and post it.

That was a totally generic tweet and not pointed at any specific person, site, or Facebook page. A broadcast meteorologist in Savannah used the "drunk monkey" line on the air with a specific reference to some guy in Florida, and for some reason his followers decided to come attack me. Seems many follow the person with almost religious zeal, whether he is right or wrong.

They attacked me with vulgar profanity, spammed my social media platforms, even spammed pages of my employer and my church. The attacks on the meteorologist in Georgia were even more vitriolic. Welcome to today's world.

I understand the guy in Florida made up a "drunk donkey" t-shirt and sold piles of them. Guess he is, if nothing else, a good businessman.

We spend time that we don't have dealing with social media disinformation campaigns. I actually know of some cases where people have cancelled an important medical appointment or a vacation trip because of a model map they saw on their Facebook feed involving a high impact event 10-15 days out. And, of course, that event never happened, and they were demanding to know why we got it wrong. On some days I get dozens of private messages asking me if "this is true," with a link to some wild forecast full of hyperbole.

The bottom line is this. If you see a wild forecast concerning a big event weeks away from some Facebook site like "Uncle Joe's Tot Locker and Weather Page," please DON'T share or like.

CHAPTER 28
EF-5 FLYOVER; ANOTHER CLOSE CALL WITH DEATH

After a short nap, I was back at ABC 33/40 at 5:00 a.m. April 9, 1998. We boarded "AirLink 33/40," the station helicopter, to fly over the damaged path of the violent tornado that had moved through western Jefferson County the night before. Understand, nobody really knew how bad it was in darkness; that would be revealed at the first light of day when we would be over the path beaming back live video to our viewers in Alabama. I told the pilot to begin at Oak Grove School, where we knew there was serious damage. We arrived there shortly after 6:00, and the scene below was worse than I imagined. I spent much time in that school building over the years doing weather programs, and to see nothing but a flattened pile of steel and concrete was horrifying.

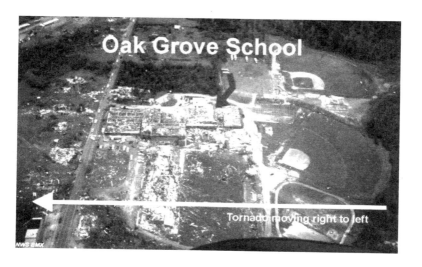

From there, it certainly didn't get any better. Rock Creek, Sylvan Springs, Edgewater, McDonald Chapel, and Pratt City looked like bombed-out war zones. We could see people waving red flags at us, meaning they were in immediate need of aid or medical assistance. We could only hope relief agencies were watching so they could dispatch the needed crews.

As we found the end of the damaged path in Pratt City, we turned around for one more flyover, this time going from northeast to southwest. About the time we were over Rock Creek, I heard the pilot, a Vietnam veteran, say a very rare expletive, and the chopper dropped like a rock a few seconds later. During that rapid descent, that didn't last for more than 5-10 seconds, my mind started to race. Is there an engine problem? Are we about to crash?

Once we leveled off again, the pilot told me we just missed an air-to-air collision with another helicopter by a distance of less than 100 yards. By the look on his face, I knew that was a serious situation. He later told me it was nothing short of a miracle he spotted the other chopper, and we were both lucky to be alive. Seems like the guy in the other chopper wanted to be the first with aerial video of the damage and didn't go through the proper procedure to let other air traffic know he was in the area.

Like the September 1978 incident on I-59/20 near Tuscaloosa, I escaped death again in 1998. Why God chooses to take some home at a very early age and leave others here for a long time will always be a mystery. I just figured I had work to do, and I did want to see my two boys grow up. I am thankful to this day I am here; every day is truly a gift.

A few days later, President Clinton visited Birmingham to personally see the tornado aftermath. For some reason, the station had me live with a variety of news anchors and reporters during the visit; I was positioned at Edgewater, right by the President's scheduled procession. I guess they figured I could talk for a long time if they needed someone to fill air time.

While I was on the air, live on ABC 33/40, I noticed out of the corner of my eye some guy coming toward me pretty quickly, and he didn't look happy. As he got closer, I was sure hoping one of the crew members would restrain him and keep him from getting to me. But that never happened. He just kept coming.

I noticed there was a sharpshooter, in camouflage, on the roof of a house adjacent to my location. Maybe that guy could just hit him in the leg and take him down before he did something to me. But, he was completely focused on protecting the President and had no interest in the mad guy coming fast and furious at the television meteorologist.

I surely wasn't focused on what I was saying on the air; my heart was beating out of my chest, knowing some guy was about to walk right into the shot and hurt me. I didn't know why he would be mad; I figured he was a troll, hater, or know-it-all with guts.

Sure enough, he walked right into the shot while I was on the air. But, instead of hurting me, the guy looked me right in the eyes and said some very kind words about our coverage of the tornado April 8 and how it helped him to take care of his family. He was simply glad to be alive, wanted me to know and gave me a big hug. All live on ABC 33/40.

Understand, I was pretty tired, but more relieved he wasn't mad and didn't do anything to us. I stopped and hugged him back, and we both shed a few tears. Needless to say, it was some interesting live television.

The guy that walked into the shot was Jeff Blankenship, and we have become friends over the years. I still enjoy going to lunch with Jeff from time to time, and we both get some good laughs about that incident. Jeff especially giggles about the mullet hairstyle he had back then.

The EF-5 tornado would be responsible for 32 deaths; the EF-2 in St. Clair County, east of Birmingham, killed 2. One of the 34 killed was 8-year-old Nathan Seals. Nathan, his parents, and two siblings, lived in Rock Creek. The family heard the warning and went to the safest place in their home, but the EF-5 monster wiped the home off the foundation, and lofted the entire family. Nathan died from his injuries, but the rest of the family survived.

On the day of Nathan's funeral, his family was brought in by paramedics. Although they were still badly injured, they wanted to be there for the funeral of their son and brother.

It is very important to note that physicians later told the family that Nathan would have survived if he had had on any kind of helmet. For that very reason, we continue to push the importance of wearing any kind of helmet if people are in a tornado warning polygon. Almost any helmet will suffice - a baseball batting helmet, football helmet, etc. Wearing head protection will greatly enhance the chances of surviving a tornado.

Nathan's dad, Matthew, became a close personal friend in the coming years. Matthew Seals would go with us occasionally on our spring weather tours across Alabama, speaking on the importance of wearing a helmet during a tornado warning. At first, I thought God put him in my life so I could encourage him. But, the truth is that he was put in my life to encourage me. I have appreciated his friendship in many ways.

CHAPTER 29
SUSPENDERS AND THE CLOTHING SCALE

I was always a skinny guy during my high school, college, and young adult years. My pal, Dave Baird often said I would have been a good model for toothpick manufacturers. I tried everything: milkshakes, eating four meals a day. I just couldn't gain weight.

Then came my 40s. All of a sudden, here came the pounds, fast and furious. Like a freight train. I was up 25 pounds in a year or so, and my clothes didn't fit. So, I went to the time, trouble, and expense of buying a new wardrobe for my larger body. This all happened in the 1999-2000 time frame.

I came to the brilliant conclusion that I needed to make some lifestyle and dietary adjustments and get a little of that weight off. And, magically, about 10 pounds were shed. But, alas, my new suits were too big around the waist. I sure wasn't going to spend any more money on clothes. One idea was to buy braces to keep my big pants from falling down while I was on the job. Turns out it worked like magic, and that was the beginning of the signature "James Spann look" in early 2000.

I usually wear simple, dark suspenders with the TV suits, but on occasion I will bring out colorful ones for Christmas and other special occasions. I actually thought about using color-coded suspenders based on the severe weather threat level for the day, but that seemed too corny.

How many pairs of suspenders do I have? No real idea, but I would guess over 50 at the station alone.

As it turns out, a perception would soon begin that might even be a better severe weather indicator. Anyone who has been in a television studio knows it gets hot after the lights have been on for several hours, especially with the older lights we used before 2010. As a result of that heat, I had the habit of shedding my jacket, and at some point rolling up my sleeves to beat the heat during long tornado coverage, that would often go on for over six hours.

In coming years, while speaking with various groups of people in public, I learned that they noticed my state of dress during severe weather events, and figured out that the danger was especially serious when I was without a jacket and sleeves rolled up. The truth, of course, was that the studio was simply hot and uncomfortable, but I was seeing the importance of the perception. Sometime about 2010 I actually became cognizant of this and would actually hold off removing the jacket or rolling up the sleeves until the weather was really dangerous.

It remains part of my routine to this day. The "James Spann clothing scale" is a real thing now.

For those that know me well, I am not a guy who likes to dress up. My real life look is wearing a t-shirt and cargo shorts. Lame, I know, but that is the look. Anyone can find me in those shorts even during the middle of winter, away from the world of TV.

CHAPTER 30
DECEMBER 16, 2000

The year 1999 was fairly quiet in terms of severe weather in Alabama, but things really began to shake and bake from 2000 to 2002. One of the biggest events came on December 16, 2000, when an EF-4 tornado tore through the southern part of the city of Tuscaloosa.

That event was a challenge in that it happened on a Saturday nine days before Christmas. We were short staffed, and reaching people during the height of the holiday shopping season is very difficult. Again, understand that this was seven years before the iPhone was introduced; smartphone apps didn't exist then.

The warning process worked very well. A tornado watch was issued at 10:00 that morning, almost three hours before the tornado first touched down at 12:54 p.m. A tornado warning was put out by the Birmingham National Weather Service office at 12:40 p.m., and that was when we went into wall–to–wall coverage. I was with Mark Prater in the weather office, and shortly before 1:00 Mark spotted the big twister on our Tower Cam on the old WCFT tower in the eastern part of Tuscaloosa. I was on the air and at the same time listening to reports via amateur radio on the 146.82 MHz amateur radio repeater in Tuscaloosa. When Mark said, "There it is, James;" all of our attention jumped to the live video.

It was the first tornado captured on live camera video for us and made for some intense live television. I knew the video would tell the story, but I also had to be very descriptive since we were being simulcast on a number of radio stations in West Alabama. The size of the big wedge was increasing as it got closer, moving into the southern part of the city of Tuscaloosa near Shelton State Community College and Hillcrest High School.

Unfortunately, at the time the camera controls in the newsroom were on the other side of the building. Garry Kelly, the news director, was actually the one working the controls, and of course, at the same time, he was dispatching crews to the scene and handling a variety of other chores related to news coverage. Garry's inexperience with the complex camera controls, and all of the distractions, made for some less than stellar live camera moves. It even prompted Mark to say, "Let's get someone who knows how to work that camera over there," not knowing it was his boss running things. That situation, by the way, was the genesis of the SKYCAM system we use today, with full zoom, pan, and tilt controls in the weather office at our fingertips.

Another drama was taking place in the tornado path. John Oldshue was in our storm chaser van, which at the time was a large conversion van put together by my friend Rod McSweeney at Southern Comfort Conversions. While that van was indeed the definition of comfort, it was not the best choice for a storm chase vehicle due to its high profile nature.

John was in the eastern part of the city, along with ABC 33/40 photographer Cyril Samonte. After realizing they were in the direct path, they abruptly stopped their video work and sought shelter in a Hampton Inn. Thankfully, someone from management unlocked the doors and allowed them in; the storm chase van was nearly totaled.

That tornado was rated an F4 on the Fujita Scale for tornado intensity. Tornado intensity varied along the path with considerable F2 and F3 damage in the area from just west of SR 69 to US 82 in the Hinton Place and Hillcrest Meadows areas as well as in the Bear Creek area. It was also in those areas where pockets of F4 destruction occurred. Tornadoes are rated with the highest F-scale rating along the track. An update to the original F-scale was implemented on February 1, 2007, and is now known as the EF-scale.

A total of eleven people were killed that day, most of those around the Bear Creek trailer park. A remarkable image was captured by *Tuscaloosa News* photographer Michael E. Palmer showing a man, Michael Harris, carrying an unconscious Whitney Crowder, 6, through debris in the Bear Creek Trailer Park after the tornado passed through. Whitney's father and 15-month-old brother were killed.

There are so many heroes in the moments following a tornado, and most get no credit for their actions. Harris has never wanted any publicity, but I think this photo captures the remarkable human spirit that seems to surge over all of our differences on occasion.

In May 2012 I received an invitation from Whitney, who was about to graduate from Tuscaloosa County High School. Today we can celebrate Whitney's life because of special people like Michael Harris. These are the special stories. Congratulations to Whitney for her example of growing  up as a young woman of character after enduring a horrible near-death experience at the age of 6.

CHAPTER 31
SCHOOL VISITS

As I recall, my first weather program in a school was at St. Francis Xavier School in Birmingham in the fall of 1979. It was not spectacular, but it started something that is a part of my daily routine that still energizes me today.

I honestly have no idea how many schools I have visited since St. Frances Xavier. Unless I have something work related to do, I visit one or two schools every weekday. This is a win-win for all: kids learn science, and they get to know me and usually seek me out on TV. I also learn the geography of the state of Alabama. I like to take the "roads less traveled" when time allows, and after almost 40 years of these school programs, I have a sharp knowledge of the people, geography, and culture of this state.

I have talked with students all the way from pre-K to the college graduate level. But, my strength is grades 1 through 5. These are my people: I understand them, and they understand me. Occasionally a teacher will introduce me to a student with a very strong interest in weather; I always invite that student to come up to the station on a Friday afternoon to watch the newscasts in the studio and get a tour. This experience has led to more than a few professional careers in meteorology over the years.

In the early days, I would lug around a slide projector; then it morphed into a laptop with digital content in the 1990s. The kids learn about instruments, weather maps, radar and satellite data, and how we do upper air soundings. But they love the lightning, tornado, and snow video. I do understand some children have a genuine fear of storms and tornadoes, but information is very powerful. I do my best to channel the content so that they understand that storms are good, and while tornadoes are indeed bad, they just don't happen that often. If they understand them and know what to do, the kids will be just fine.

Safety is also a big push in schools; students learn not only where to go, but also what to do. Like, wearing helmets in their safe place. Wearing hard sole shoes and having a portable air horn so first responders can find them if they are hit by a tornado. And trust me, the students I see know never to rely on an outdoor warning siren.

On occasion, I will stick around and enjoy a meal in the lunchroom. I have become Alabama's expert on school lunches, and let me say up front that the lunchroom ladies make the world go around. They see every student every day and often give an encouraging word or smile that is so needed. Despite the somewhat insane federal guidelines, the lunches are the best buy in town. There is only one food that I don't recommend in a school lunchroom . . . chicken fajitas. I advise kids if they see them being served, to immediately run and call 911! Everything else is great; how could anyone not love a square pizza coming from a school lunchroom?

And, there is some real talent in these places. I have seen kids. . .

*Put Nestles Quick in their mouths with some milk, and make chocolate milk come out of their noses. Worst part is that they then drink it. Now that is nasty.

*Drink some milk, slosh it around in their mouths, hold their breath until their face turns red, and then drops of milk come out of their tear ducts. How in the world does that work? And, why would any child learn to do it?

*Launch a single roll all the way across the lunchroom, bouncing off the wall and into a trash receptacle. The kids who can do this probably wind up in the NBA

When they say, "Hey Mr. James. . .watch this. . ." you know something special is coming. I will always cherish and laugh at the lunchroom adventures I have enjoyed over the years. By the way, my advice, which is true for any school lunchroom: avoid chicken fajitas. Everything else is safe. And, a shout to the lunchroom ladies. As I said before, they make the world go around and have a wonderful ministry. They see every child every day and often know more about the lives of those kids than anyone else.

CHAPTER 32
INTERNS AND BUSY TORNADO SEASONS

My first summer college interns were John Oldshue and Mike O'Lenick at WBRC in the early 1990s. John would go on to work with me at ABC 33/40, and Mike settled into Central Florida, where he did weather in Orlando for many years. Both John and Mike majored in Geoscience/Meteorology at Mississippi State University.

No way do I have the space here to write about all of the interns under my watch over the years, but I am proud of all of them. They are scattered in television markets around the nation and are very successful.

One interesting story involved a young woman who spent the summer of 2000 with us; she was a student in the meteorology program at Valparaiso University in Indiana. Her academics were strong, work ethic was excellent, and she had an unusually strong on camera presence for her age. She moved to Birmingham for the summer, and worked as a lifeguard at Heatherwood Country Club to pay for her apartment. Today, most people watch her every weekday on Good Morning America -- Ginger Zee. She is the chief meteorologist for ABC News and is a remarkable role model for young women interested in science.

Ginger had a very healthy diet, but we convinced her, before leaving to go back to school in Indiana, to have lunch with us one day at Dreamland in downtown Birmingham where the menu included ribs, white bread, and Dr. Pepper. Doesn't get much better.

ABC News Chief Meteorologist and former ABC 33/40
intern Ginger Zee in 2014.

For those reading this book and interested in becoming a
professional meteorologist, I can't stress the importance
of getting involved in an intern program while you are in
college. You will make connections and learn things that
are critical in the career building process.

In recent years, all of our interns must take the "Walmart
test". I take them to a big Walmart in a working class part
of Birmingham, where those in the store represent an
amazing cross section of those who watch our television
station. For the college students, generally speaking, most
of these people don't look like them, don't think like
them, don't vote like they do, and are much older. If the
interns can't make a good connection face-to-face with
these people, they will fail trying to communicate weather
across television or some digital platform. You can be the

greatest scientist or forecaster, but if you don't know how to share your information with the masses, you won't be very successful. If you find those you serve to be ignorant, disgusting people, then you might consider getting into a part of the weather enterprise where you don't have to connect with people. And, quite frankly, there aren't many jobs like that.

So often I attend weather conferences, and we sit around in big rooms trying to figure what is right for us. The truth is, we have to figure out what is right for our audience. We need to spend more time in the Walmarts and Dollar Generals of the world to learn more about connecting with the real end users we serve.

In the early 2000s, most of the tornadoes in Alabama came during the late fall season in November and December. November 24, 2001 was an interesting day. It was the Saturday over the long Thanksgiving holiday weekend, and we were very thinly staffed. It looked like a fairly routine type severe weather threat, and instead of calling people back in from vacation, I asked our son, J.P., who was 17 at the time, to come in and help me in the office and run radar just in case a tornado warning was issued.

J.P. got more work in that day that he bargained for. And, for a high school student, he did an exemplary job under much pressure. As it turned out, we had over two dozen tornadoes in the state, and a total of four were killed... two in Lamar County near Millport, and two in Cherokee County near Sand Rock. One of the tornadoes was a strong/violent EF-4 that moved through parts of Blount and Etowah Counties.

EF-4 tornado December 16, 2000 moving through Tuscaloosa. ABC 33/40 coverage screen grab.

Then, one year later, on November 10, 2002, we had the Veterans Day tornado outbreak, which produced 10 tornadoes, killing 11 people. The deaths were mostly in Walker County from a pair of EF-3 twisters that were parallel to each other and only about one hour apart. That was on a Sunday night, making it very hard to show live video of these tornadoes. But John Oldshue did an excellent job in the field, showing the non-stop lightning output from the EF-3s in Walker County from the storm chaser van (yep, same one that was almost totaled in Tuscaloosa in December 2000).

ABC 33/40 was only six years old in November 2002, but our weather operation had become a mature, well organized operation that was critical to the severe weather warning process across North/Central Alabama. We were far from perfect, but we were getting it mostly right on long-form weather coverage. All of this experience, and I mean every bit of it, would be needed nine years later.

CHAPTER 33
TROPICAL TROUBLES

My market is Birmingham/Tuscaloosa/Anniston, about 200 miles north of the Gulf Coast, close enough to have a big impact from landfalling tropical systems, including gradient wind, flooding, and tornadoes. Some might recall that Hurricane Frederic blew through Alabama during my first week on the air in Birmingham in September 1979, but the Central Gulf Coast was relatively unscathed during much of the 1980s and 1990s.

Hurricane Elena did the hokey-pokey off the Gulf Coast in 1985 when I was in Dallas; that thing was seemingly headed for the Florida "Big Bend" region north of Tampa Bay, but it pretty much whipped a U and abruptly changed directions, ultimately making landfall near Biloxi, Mississippi.

Seven years later, after wreaking havoc in Southern Florida, Hurricane Andrew made a second landfall in a sparsely populated part of the Louisiana coast near Morgan City in 1992. I was dispatched by WBRC to cover the second coming of Andrew. I did my live shot the night before landfall in downtown New Orleans with photographer Phil Mandley. For safety reasons, it was determined that we should move the satellite truck across Lake Pontchartrain to Slidell during landfall. That was before Live U technology. We needed that big truck to go live, but with the dish raised, it was extremely unsafe during hurricanes. We heard of severe damage in LaPlace, Louisiana, west of New Orleans, where a tornado touched down in a spiral band rotating around the center of Andrew.

Phil and I headed for LaPlace from New Orleans, and indeed, there was very significant damage, although it was difficult to determine the extent since this was during the pre-dawn hours. The eye of Andrew was approaching, and I made a bone-headed decision to pull the satellite truck from Slidell over to LaPlace, with the thought of going live on our early morning news while the eye was overhead, providing favorable conditions for a satellite shot. That would make the news management happy-- being live from a heavily damaged area during an important newscast.

Unfortunately, just before the live shot was scheduled, the eye wall approached more rapidly than we expected, and conditions started to deteriorate. Remember, this is 1992, long before you could pull up a radar app on a smartphone and before wireless Internet access. Pretty much the best you could do was CompuServe or Prodigy on a 300 baud phone modem. And, that was no help in the middle of a hurricane.

The satellite truck operator brought down the dish in the wind and rain and headed back down I-10 toward New Orleans. Phil was in the back of the satellite truck, editing tape shot in LaPlace, and I was driving a news car, praying the three of us could get back to a safe place, where we could feed video and file my report.

Harold Stanfield, the satellite truck operator, for some reason slowed down and pulled over on the shoulder of

I-10 west of Metairie, and I pulled in behind them. By this time, weather conditions were brutal, with wind gusts near hurricane force and blinding, tropical rain with visibility less than a fraction of a mile. In these conditions, Harold got out of the cab and came over to me, letting me know that the engine had conked out and the truck was dead in the water.

My worry about feeding video and making a report changed to a concern for our safety. I figured we needed to abandon the satellite truck; I told Harold and Phil to get in the news car so we could get back to a safe place to ride out that back eye wall. When things calmed down we could call a tow truck and get the satellite truck repaired. And, I must admit, I feared for my job since I made the bad call to move the truck in the middle of Andrew's landfall.

But, Harold said to "wait a cotton picking minute." He got into the satellite truck engine, in hurricane force wind gusts and driving rain, and after about 10 minutes we heard the magical sound of the engine starting up in the big truck. I have no idea what he did, or how he did it, but we were back in business and rolling again. We made it through New Orleans, across Lake Pontchartrain, and back to Slidell, where I did a live shot and filed the report during the tail end of our morning news.

I worked many a storm with Harold Stanfield in my years at WBRC and somehow, he always got us on the air on time. He is one of the many unsung heroes I have worked with. The engineers and photographers actually do most of the work and rarely get much of the credit.

More than 10 years after Hurricane Andrew would come, the busy hurricane seasons of 2004/2005 arrived. Hurricane Ivan, in September 2004, was a classic Cape Verde storm; it formed from a wave that moved off the coast of Africa and made the long journey across the Atlantic. It achieved category five status in the Caribbean and Southern Gulf of Mexico but weakened to a category three with sustained winds of 130 mph as it slammed into the Alabama Gulf Coast during the pre-dawn hours on September 16.

Despite the weakening, there was severe damage from storm surge and wind on the Alabama Gulf Coast. We had some scary moments when we lost contact with two members of our crew: Chief Photographer Bill Castle, and reporter Christopher Sign, who is now our primary weeknight news anchor at ABC 33/40. The storm surge cut them off, and they had to ride out the storm basically in the stairwell of a condominium complex in Gulf Shores. There is a high chance that those two guys were the only humans on the immediate Alabama coast during landfall, and we lost radio contact with them during the height of the storm.

After my experience with Frederic in 1979, I had a pretty good idea of what those guys were dealing with. Being exposed like that in a category three hurricane is dangerous and life-threatening.

Up in Birmingham we were in long-form coverage. As I recall, we did wall-to-wall weather for about 18 hours that day, which is possibly the longest green wall stint in my career. Ivan brought the risk of gradient wind damage, flooding and tornadoes to inland parts of the state, so we were excessively busy. But, the behind the scene drama was playing out as we tried to find out the condition of Castle and Sign. At some point in the morning, we got word that they were found safe by the Gulf Shores police and were on a boat headed for higher ground. We had a live crew along Alabama 59 at Waterville, where the Little Lagoon had taken over the highway, and they were able to reunite with Bill and Christopher at that point. We put Chris on the air to talk with me, and that was when we had an overwhelming sense of relief knowing those two guys made it through the storm.

Ivan dealt a huge blow to Alabama. At one point almost half a million people were without power; some would not see electrical service restored for over three weeks. Winds reached 90 mph at Demopolis, over 100 miles inland, and parts of the Birmingham metro received over 10 inches of rain. Blue tarps were seen on roofs over the southern half of the state for months.

The next year, we had the most active hurricane season on record in the Atlantic basin. In 2005, there were 28 named storms, 15 hurricanes, and 7 major hurricanes. The strongest was Wilma with sustained winds of 185 mph at one point and a central pressure of 882 mb. But for the Central Gulf Coast, the big story was Hurricane Katrina. Like Ivan the year before, Katrina reached category five strength in the Southern Gulf of Mexico but would weaken to a category three at the time of landfall.

New Orleans, of course, got the main national attention due to over 50 failures of the levees and floodwalls protecting the city, leading to catastrophic flooding. Many in Mississippi felt that they were ignored by the media, and they had a valid complaint. Damage on the Mississippi coast was widespread and severe and resulted in great human suffering.

In Alabama, the storm surge from Katrina cut a new canal through the western part of Dauphin Island, but thankfully coastal communities in Baldwin County, and places like Gulf Shores and Orange Beach, didn't suffer the extreme kind of damage seen during Ivan. But inland, once again about a half a million people had no power, and were dealing with gradient wind damage, flooding, and a few tornadoes.

CHAPTER 34
APRIL 2011

Alabama has two distinct tornado seasons--spring, and late fall. Severe thunderstorms are most likely during the months of March, April, and May and in November and December. Of these five months, April averages more than the rest. And, that was certainly true in 2011.

April 2011, an incredibly active month for severe thunderstorms, was within a global climate context of lingering La Niña conditions (cold phase of the Southern Oscillation). On April 4, 2011, a number of severe thunderstorms moved across the state, producing scattered wind damage and some flooding.

One week later, on April 11, more severe storms rolled through Alabama. A quasi-linear convective system (a fancy phrase for what we called a squall line in the old days) produced an EF-1 tornado with winds estimated at 100 mph in the city of Vestavia Hills, a suburb just south of Birmingham. The path was 0.4 miles long and 100 yards wide. The tornado touched down near the Vestavia Hills Police Department along U.S. Highway 31 and traveled northeast.

After that April 11 severe weather day, we didn't get much time to rest.

A three-day severe weather outbreak unfolded April 14, 15, and 16. There were a total of 178 tornadoes across 16 states. Those tornadoes were responsible for killing 38 people; five more died from straight line winds associated with severe thunderstorms.

In Alabama, 45 tornadoes tore through the southern two-thirds of the state on April 15. These tornadoes were responsible for four deaths: one in Marengo County and three in Autauga County. One of the tornadoes, an EF-3, developed that afternoon in the far southwest corner of Tuscaloosa County. It moved northeast, as most tornadoes do in Alabama, ultimately impacting the southern and eastern parts of the city of Tuscaloosa. It was on the ground for 18 miles and was 500 yards wide at its widest point. There was an excellent warning for this storm, and there were no deaths or injuries. It did leave considerable damage, however, with many homes and businesses impacted.

We call this event the "forgotten" tornado outbreak. It was one of the largest in Alabama history, yet most people today don't recall it because of what happened 12 days later. The event was a harbinger, almost as if the atmosphere was talking to us, giving us a clue of what was to come.

Five days later, more severe storms. A slow moving cold front caused two rounds of severe thunderstorms across Alabama on Wednesday, April 20, producing widespread damaging winds and rainfall that led to isolated incidents of flooding. On the morning forecast discussion I wrote for our blog (http://www.alabamawx.com), after going through the set-up for severe weather over the next 24 hours, I wrote the following:

Sure looks like a significant severe weather event is ahead, initially west of Alabama Tuesday, then moving into the Deep South by Tuesday night and Wednesday. Way too early to be specific on the threat, but all of the players are on the field. Best hope for us is for the band of storms to come through during the pre-dawn hours Wednesday when the air tends to be more stable, but I get the idea it might be an event mainly during the daytime Wednesday. See the Weather Xtreme video for details.

Seven days out, computer models were already giving signals of yet another severe weather threat for Alabama that would be "significant." Not sure many people really noted that part of the discussion, but it was clearly the most important thing I wrote on that post.

Once we got past the April 20 event, we could focus on what might happen on April 27. I wrote the following on Friday, April 22:

Still looks like a significant severe weather event coming up for the southern U.S. The problems begin early in the week to the west; showers and storms could arrive in Alabama as early as Tuesday, but the main event seems to be Wednesday, and the 12Z GFS hints that all modes of severe weather will be possible; cellular supercell storms Wednesday afternoon, followed by a squall line with potential for damaging winds Wednesday night. And, heavy rain will be an issue as well. We will keep an eye on this over the weekend and have a detailed look by Monday.

After a warm, dry weekend with highs in the 80s, on Monday it was very clear that Wednesday would be a big, severe weather day for Alabama, potentially a "red letter" kind of day. These were my words on Monday April 25:

The primary threat of tornadoes will come on Wednesday afternoon, when supercells will begin to form across North and Central Alabama as the cap breaks. Forecast wind profiles and instability values suggest a few strong, long-track tornadoes will be possible across the northern half of Alabama Wednesday afternoon into the evening hours.

Then, Wednesday night, everything will merge into a long squall line with potential for wind damage. Everything should be out of the state soon after midnight Wednesday night.

*WILL WEDNESDAY BE AN HISTORIC WEATHER DAY? I would suggest there is way too much hyperbole when it comes to stormy weather in Alabama. Some say we are guilty, but long-time readers know my concern for too much "hype" over storms and snow in our state. SPC [Storm Prediction Center] does have most of North and Central Alabama in a moderate risk of severe weather.

It is important to simply understand this is April in Alabama, when we expect severe weather outbreaks. Yes, just about all forecast parameters suggest potential for a widespread severe weather event here, but I would not say "historic" at this point. We have another 24-30 hours to review data before we get too carried away here. There is no need to be alarmed. . .just be able to hear warnings, and have a plan, and you will be just fine.

With the explosive growth of social media comes the ocean of weather hype and disinformation. Armchair meteorologists (we call them "social media-rologists") ramp up the verbiage before big weather days; they have learned extreme hyperbole associated with "death, doom, destruction" forecasts will get the most likes, shares, and clicks. One role of professional meteorologists is now to put down all the hype and give a level-headed forecast that includes timing, risk, and uncertainty. We all know that April 27 was an historic event now, but I didn't want people to panic. Understand we had a huge tornado day back on April 15, and many were suffering from severe weather fatigue and anxiety. I wanted people to get ready for a big day without unnecessary fear. Their great concern if I used "historic" at that point in the preparation forecast would not be productive.

This was part of my afternoon blog discussion on Tuesday, April 26. It was written shortly after 3:00 that afternoon:

DANGEROUS SEVERE WEATHER THREAT TOMORROW: Watch the video and you will see all of the synoptic elements for a major outbreak are in place. A deep (sub-1000 mb) low west of Memphis, steep lapse rates, strong veering of the wind with altitude in respect to projected storm motion, strong wind fields at the surface and aloft, dry air in the midlevels, and a very deep, long wave upper trough that is somewhat negatively tilted enhancing diffluence aloft over Alabama.

Projected soundings show the classic "loaded gun" look, meaning that a cap should keep storms at bay through the morning hours, but when that cap breaks early in the afternoon, storms will quickly become severe with all modes of severe weather possible. This means potential for large hail, damaging winds, and a few violent, long-track tornadoes. This is dangerous weather setup.

Of course, long-time readers know that mesoscale features play a huge role in the ultimate severity of a severe weather day, and we really won't know about those until early tomorrow.

TIMING: This is an event where it doesn't make much sense to ask when storms will arrive in your county or home town; nobody knows since the initial storms will be cellular in nature. Just understand a severe storm is basically possible anytime from now through 3:00 a.m. Thursday. The storms tonight will mostly pose a threat of high winds and large hail, although an isolated tornado cannot be ruled out.

Tomorrow, the main risk comes from about 12:00 noon to 12:00 midnight. Again, we can't rule out morning storms, but the most intense and dangerous thunderstorms will come during the afternoon and nighttime hours. The severe storms should merge a long squall line late tomorrow night, with the main threat becoming damaging straight line winds after 10:00 p.m. or so.

REMEMBER: With potential for some severe weather today, and a red letter kind of severe weather day possible tomorrow, be sure you are in a position to hear severe weather warnings (never rely on a siren!) and have a good plan of action when warnings are issued. No need to panic; even large tornadoes are small compared to a large county. But, we must be prepared.

SCHOOLS: For school systems that do decide to dismiss early tomorrow, please consider giving students that live in mobile homes the option of staying in school buildings. In many rural parts of the state those school buildings are absolutely the safest place.

I believe the entire weather enterprise did a very good job in communicating the potential danger for Alabama in the days leading up to April 27. I used every tool in the shed; TV, radio, blogs, apps, and the social platforms available at the time. The screaming message was that a major severe thunderstorm/tornado day was likely, and people needed to get ready. Some listened; some didn't.

I got home about midnight Tuesday night and as usual, had a hard time getting to sleep. But, I knew some rest was a necessity. All of the severe weather parameters were in place for a major outbreak, but I still didn't know what would happen. Could it be a high risk bust? If so, would people forgive me for crying wolf? Or, could it be a day that goes down in history books? Will people lose their lives? Did I do enough to get people ready? I finally drifted off to sleep about 1:00 a.m.

CHAPTER 35
APRIL 27

Most people have only one or two days in their lives that define them. All cumulative experiences in life, both good and bad, will weave together to prepare people. And, they really never know when they wake up in the morning that that particular day is going to define them.

One of mine came on April 27, 2011. I do believe I was born to be standing in front of a big green wall in a television studio that day. Why me? I have no idea. But it was some kind of destiny.

I can think of so many things that led me to that day: the book I read in first grade; the intense curiosity with the thunderstorms on summer afternoons as a young boy in Butler County; the fear and desperation that I saw in the emergency room of the small hospital in Jasper during the Super Outbreak in 1974; the work ethic I developed after my father left that led to a career in meteorology. Without these, I would not have been in the weather office that Wednesday.

My alarm is set for 4:52 every weekday morning. It gives me a few minutes to get some coffee, read a Bible verse or two, and get my brain in order for the day ahead. Understand, I work basically from 5:00 a.m. until 11:00 p.m. weekdays, so long hours are nothing special or unusual for me. Also, we are in the midst of a very tornado-prone area, and aggressive, long-form, severe weather coverage is nothing new. But nothing could have really prepared me for the intensity and pressure of that day.

On April 27, it wasn't the usual phone alarm that woke me up, but a notification at 4:13 a.m. that a tornado warning had been issued for Pickens County in West Alabama. I knew that a few storms early in the day could be strong to severe but had planned on most of my work coming later in the day and into the night. But there was no time to think. . . I had to get to work in a hurry. After a two minute shower, and a 15 second toothbrush session, I put on a suit, grabbed the keys, and took off.

The regular drive from our home to the ABC 33/40 studio is usually 25-30 minutes. I can't say for sure, but I believe I made it in 15 minutes that morning. I figured if a law enforcement officer stopped me, he might give me a pass considering the seriousness of the situation.

When I zipped into the ABC 33/40 studio, in Riverchase (a development in Hoover, about 12 miles south of downtown Birmingham), my colleague Jason Simpson was on the big green wall, at the top of his game, passing on critical information, with no help. He had been flying solo for over two hours . . . we wanted to give most of the staff a little rest in preparation for the big part of the event later that day and into the night.

Jason and I stayed on the air until 9:00 a.m.; that is when everything calmed down and all warnings had expired. But the morning got rougher than expected. A long line of severe storms, with embedded tornadoes, rolled through the state, killing 5 people and injuring over 50. There was widespread damage from straight line winds, and a dozen tornadoes touched down. One of them was an EF-2 in the Birmingham metro. . .it crossed busy U.S. 280 and moved through Cahaba Heights a little before 6:00 a.m.

It is important to note that the morning round of storms was responsible for knocking out power to almost a quarter of a million people in Alabama; that would present more challenges in our ability to warn people of tornadoes later in the day.

After the long-form weather coverage ended and we pitched over to Studio D for our show "Talk of Alabama," I looked at Jason, and he looked at me, but we didn't say anything. It was almost like someone had punched us in the gut without any warning. And, before we could say much, the studio was flooded with engineers letting us know that the station had suffered a good bit of infrastructure damage. Among the problems included the loss of some of our live SKYCAMs, and microwave path outages that impacted our ability to put people on the air out in the field.

I finally told the guys to stop. Knowing we had potential for a catastrophic afternoon and tonight ahead, I needed to know what WAS working. And, I gave them a good sense of priority on the things that needed repair and restoration. Those engineers deserve credit. Ron Thomas and his team did a remarkable job of restoring SKYCAMs and microwave channels for us during a very short midday lull.

Over the next hour we could plan afternoon coverage. Meteorologist Ashley Brand was in the field in our Storm Chaser, our main volunteer chaser, John Brown, would be with Mike Wilhelm in West Alabama, and John Oldshue, who had retired from professional meteorology, liked to help on big days and was with Ben Greer in the western part of the state as well.

During that midday break, I did take a few minutes to go back into my office. I closed the door, put my head down on my desk, and prayed, asking God for wisdom, strength, and endurance. All three were needed to make it through the rest of the day and the core of the event.

Shortly after 1:00, as anticipated, new storms were firing. One was north of Jasper and started to take on the familiar kidney-bean shape on radar. We let the studio crew know we were about to go on the air at any minute, and there was a good chance we would be in wall-to-wall weather coverage for an extended period of time. Understand, without a director, audio operator, and studio crew, there would be no coverage. They get no glory or thanks, but they did an exemplary job under extreme pressure on April 27. In weather, we have no scripts; everything is done on the fly. The production crew doesn't know what we will do next, what video we will call for, or what source is needed. That day they were at the top of their game, knowing that people were watching Alabama history through their switcher, audio console, and studio cameras.

I should also mention that our engineering staff did a stunning job of getting cameras, microwave paths, and

Internet connections restored by the time the afternoon storms fired. They, too, have a thankless job.

We broke into regular programming about 1:45 when a PDS (particularly dangerous situation) tornado watch was issued, and we were there to stay. I didn't even think about who we ticked off by covering *General Hospital*; this was serious business, and if someone had an issue with our long-form coverage on this day, they weren't worth my time.

A tornado warning was issued by Cullman County at 2:24, and as the storm approached the city of 25,000 people, our SKYCAM was pointed right at the storm. We always take it on the air to complement radar coverage. Most severe storms in Alabama are HP (heavy precipitation) supercells and tornadoes associated with them are rain wrapped. That, combined with the hills and trees means people generally won't be able to see much.

But, to our surprise, the right rear flank of the storm was pretty much clear of rain, and we could see what was clearly a funnel cloud, if not a tornado, with the storm a good 10 miles southwest of Cullman and 12 miles southwest of our SKYCAM site at the city water treatment plant. Within no time at all we could see it was indeed a tornado, and a large one, complete with debris. We then called a "tornado emergency," the highest level of weather alert we use. A confirmed tornado was down, we were looking at it, and it was a severe threat to life. The message was simple:

> "If you live in Good Hope or Cullman, go to a
> small room, on the lowest floor, near the center of

the house, and away from windows NOW. Do not get into a car, and get out of mobile homes. You do not have to be underground to survive."

We stayed exclusively with the live SKYCAM video until power was lost at the water treatment plant, right after the tornado crossed U.S. 31 in downtown Cullman. Before we lost the feed, we were able to see the free standing tower by First Baptist Church collapse, and parts of the Cullman County Courthouse being lofted. It was graphic violence live on television. But it had to be shown as people react so much better to live video of a tornado.

Our hard-working associates over in the newsroom called the Cullman Regional Medical Center soon after it passed through the city, and the astonishing news was that they had no seriously injured people in their emergency room, and there were no fatalities. As I heard the report, I thought to myself . . . "the warning process is working, and people are paying attention." We had lots of damage from the morning storms, but we were operational enough to be very effective. At that time, I was very optimistic that we were going to make it without much loss of life.

Unfortunately, I was wrong.

At 2:59 p.m. a tornado warning was issued for northern Lamar and Marion counties in Northwest Alabama. By 3:10 there was a debris ball on radar with that storm, meaning the radar pulses coming from the nearby facility at Columbus (MS) Air Force Base were bouncing off debris being lofted by the storm instead of bouncing off raindrops: things like boards, bricks, glass, and nails.

These make for a high core of reflectivity which shows at the end of the traditional hook echo pattern. A tornado emergency was called for Hackleburg, and the dire message was for people there to seek shelter NOW.

The tornado was an EF-5 tornado, which is extremely rare (only 1 percent of tornadoes reach this strength), and almost always deadly. The EF (Enhanced Fujita) scale is a set of wind estimates (not measurements) based on damage. It uses three-second gusts estimated at the point of damage based on a judgment of 8 levels of damage to 28 indicators. The original "F Scale" was developed by researcher Dr. Theodore Fujita of the University of Chicago. Dr. Fujita's scale was adjusted in 2007 based on a better understanding of how tornadoes produce damage.

The damage description in the original Fujita index still tells the story of EF5 winds:

> Total destruction of buildings. Strong framed, well built houses leveled off foundations and swept away. Steel-reinforced concrete structures are critically damaged. Tall buildings collapse or have severe structural deformations.

Generally speaking, EF-5 tornadoes produce winds in excess of 200 mph. The Hackleburg tornado was responsible for the deaths of 72 people; over 140 others were injured. The tornado would stay on the ground for 132 miles through the Tennessee Valley region of North Alabama before dissipating in Franklin County, Tennessee. In Hackleburg alone, the death toll was 18. Several subdivisions, businesses and churches, along with

Hackleburg High School, Middle School, and Elementary School, and the Wrangler Plant, where many in the community were employed, were destroyed. Vehicles in Hackleburg were tossed up to 200 yards. One well-built home with 4 brick sides was completely leveled, and the debris from the home was tossed over 40 yards to the north.

Tornado damage from the April 27, 2011 outbreak.

Over the next 8 hours I dealt with more bullets from hell. There are no books, manuals, or academic papers that teach how to handle 62 tornadoes in one day. The long years of experience certainly helped, but I had no experience dealing with this kind of day on the professional side. My mind drifted back to April 1974 a time or two during the event, but there was simply no time to think. I had to react. In a way, it was beneficial; understand, I have loved ones and friends I was worried about, but the lack of time to think meant not getting emotional. People needed straight-forward, simple information presented in a bold, yet calm manner.

CHAPTER 36:
THE TUSCALOOSA/BIRMINGHAM TORNADO

I want to stress again that there were 62 tornadoes in Alabama on April 27, 2011. Unfortunately, many of the stories were never told. Especially ones of the deadly storms in rural parts of our state. The media focused on the ones that hit the population centers, which is understandable. But I regret that we simply didn't have the manpower, resources, or time to tell every story. People didn't hear much about places like Sawyerville, Eoline, Pin Hook, and Boley Springs. There was real human suffering in those communities, too. How about Cordova? Hit twice on April 27. An EF-3 tore through the town about 5:30 a.m. followed by an EF-4 about 4:30 p.m. that pretty much wiped out the entire downtown area. Among those killed in Cordova that day included 12-year-old Jonathan Doss and his 10-year-old brother Justin.

Much of the media attention was focused on the EF-4 that impacted the cities of Tuscaloosa and Birmingham. That long-lived supercell was born over eastern Mississippi; at 3:58 p.m., Alan Gerard, meteorologist in charge of the National Weather Service in Jackson, relayed a report of a large tornado on the ground in Kemper County Mississippi via National Weather Service chat, a private chat session that includes NWS and television meteorologists.

Oldshue and Greer knew that storm was headed in the general direction of Tuscaloosa, where John grew up.

They decided to position themselves in a rural part of Northeast Greene County to intercept the storm, in such a position as to provide live video of the storm back to us, so we could show it on the air. Their location, near the community of Knoxville, Alabama, turned out to be the perfect place. The massive wedge tornado moved into their camera view shortly after 4:30 p.m. which enabled us to do a number of things.

First, we know people respond more urgently when they are actually looking at live video of a tornado. It provided the confirmation for people that a large tornado was on the ground and that the threat was real, serious, and life-threatening. We called a tornado emergency for the cities of Tuscaloosa, Northport, and the University of Alabama campus. People needed to get into a safe place NOW. No telling how many lives were saved by the work of Oldshue and Greer on that day.

Understand, that urgent warning and video were about 40-45 minutes before Tuscaloosa was leveled. The average tornado warning lead time is 10-15 minutes; we just can't do much better than that.

To complicate matters, as we took John's live video of the big twister headed for Tuscaloosa, our crew in Walker County, Brian Peters and Tim Coleman, had a visual on another large, wedge tornado crossing I-22. We did not have a video stream available from them, so for a while we took the video from the tornado approaching Tuscaloosa, and the audio from Brian and Tim describing the big tornado that was approaching Cordova. That probably created some confusion, but it was the best I could do to communicate the urgency of both situations at the time. The work of Peters and Coleman, I am sure, helped to save lives in Cordova and other parts of Walker County.

While Oldshue and Greer were feeding live video back to us, there was some drama going on that viewers never knew about, and I wasn't aware of it at the time. The owner of the property was demanding that these guys leave because he thought they were on top of his septic tank lines. Oldshue tried to communicate the seriousness of the situation, and they stuck it out. We continued to show their live video of the tornado until it moved out of sight, blocked by the pine trees of West Alabama.

From there we spent most of our time using a live camera owned by ABC 33/40 atop the Tuscaloosa County Courthouse. As the storm approached the city, it was clear that a big tornado was moving in a steady state right toward the center of town. At one point, I felt compelled to say, "All you can do is pray for these people." I guess I ran out of words and just spoke from the heart. If any people in Tuscaloosa were not aware of the approaching storm, their lives were in immediate danger. There was no guarantee they would live, even if they heard the warning and did the right thing.

From our SKYCAM the world watched the tornado roll across I-359 and into Rosedale Court, a low-income housing development where there would be loss of life. Then, power went out at the Tuscaloosa County Courthouse, and we lost the live feed, showing radar as the big twister threaded the needle between Druid City

Regional Medical Center and University Mall. From there, it demolished neighborhoods in Alberta City and Holt.

Many reports of catastrophic damage would soon arrive via social media and amateur radio. We knew it was bad in Tuscaloosa, but there was no time to assess the damage. That tornado was large and violent and was staying on the ground, meaning the Birmingham metro was the next target. There was great temptation to go live to our reporters in Tuscaloosa, where there was indescribable damage, but we had to stay focused on warning people in Birmingham. This was a genuine tornado emergency.

The tornado was becoming more rain wrapped and more difficult to see. We used live dash cam video and various SKYCAMs, but we really couldn't see this monster. We had to rely on radar, which continued to show a debris ball (radar detecting debris being lofted by the tornado, producing a core of high reflectivity in the tail end of the hook echo) and an intense velocity couplet. I pleaded with people in places like Concord, Pleasant Grove, and Pratt City to get into a safe place NOW.

And, while this was happening, we had other very significant tornadoes down in rural areas, and we had to devote on-air time to them as well. There is no difference in the value of the life of a person who lives in the country and one who lives in a city.

Our SKYCAMs showed the large rain shaft that encircled the tornado as it moved through the western part of the

Birmingham area, but we didn't know if it was still down. Of course, we had to make the assumption it was down as coverage continued and damage reports kept coming. It turned out that the big twister had finally dissipated just north of downtown Birmingham and just east of Fultondale. But, the same parent supercell dropped another large, long-track tornado to the east of Birmingham, which caused loss of life and severe damage in places like Shoal Creek Valley in St. Clair County and Webster's Chapel in Calhoun County. From there it moved across southern Cherokee County, very close to the track of the Palm Sunday tornado of March 27, 1994. That one killed 20 people in the Goshen United Methodist Church during the morning worship service.

CHAPTER 37
WHAT WE NEED TO LEARN FROM APRIL 27

A total of 252 people died on April 27, 2011. That is absolutely inexcusable. In my opinion, the death toll that day should have been about 30. That is how many people heard the warning, and did the right thing. Those were precious people who died, and most didn't have to die. It was simply their day; I believe we all have a day appointed to be born and a day to die. For a reason, we will find out later in another place, their journey here was destined to end on that late April day in 2011.

But, 222 people should be here today with us. Infants, senior adults, people with high income, people with low income, people who lived in the country, and people who lived in a city. Death crossed over every socio-economic line.

How could that happen? The physical science couldn't have been any better. There were excellent warnings for all 62 tornadoes. In some cases, people had over 30 minutes lead time. If anyone told me there would be a day in my career when 252 people would die on my watch, I would say that person was as crazy as a loon!

I refused to talk about that day for six months. By chance, the National Weather Association annual meeting was in Birmingham that fall. I didn't present anything on April 27; I simply had nothing to say. I went through all of the phases of grief, including anger and depression.

Those were my people who died, and I needed time to mourn.

Today, I don't play mental gymnastics and the blame game. I am simply ready to work hard and fix what went wrong that day. What we learned was that physical science is not enough; we don't know that much about human behavior.

My first major in college was electrical engineering, and I finished in meteorology. I do know much about Alabama people and culture, but getting people to take action during a life-threatening storm is clearly something we just don't understand.

I am thankful for all of our friends in the social science community who stepped in to help us learn more about what went wrong that day and to teach us how to be better severe weather communication specialists.

History will judge me on my performance on April 27, 2011. I made mistakes. The worst was calling out "Skyland Boulevard" as a potential track for the Tuscaloosa tornado as it entered town. I had no idea that the pixels on our radar were displaced by about five miles, and that caused me to make that mistake. Lesson learned here: ALWAYS have two radar sources during life-threatening weather.

I had multiple violent, long-track tornadoes down at the same time. Which one do I focus on? Do I use a split screen? Or, split audio and video? Again, there are no rules, and I simply do what I think is right in the heat of the battle. I am hoping social scientists can continue to review those long hours of April 27 coverage and help future generations of broadcast meteorologists to be better.

I know there is blood on the hands of the weather enterprise. All of us. The false alarm radio was too high in 2011 (80 percent of tornado warnings were false alarms). The false alarms led to the cry wolf syndrome. People told us they hear tornado warnings often, but "nothing ever happens." This idea clearly led to inaction on April 27.

I am proud to say the National Weather Service in Birmingham has gotten the false alarm radio down into the 30s today; they simply went back to basic science and worked long, hard hours to make it happen. They responded beautifully to the challenge. You see, these meteorologists were heavily impacted by the loss of life as well; you just don't see or hear from them that often.

No doubt I was guilty of not stressing the importance of wearing helmets to those in tornado warning polygons. Many of those who died were lofted and killed due to shrapnel wounds to the skull. A simple bicycle or batting helmet would have saved many lives April 27.

People also needed to have a portable air horn with them in their safe place; if people are injured, they might not be able to vocalize their need for help. And, they might not be able to force enough air through a whistle. First responders are able to hear that air horn.

But, in addition to weather professionals, the public has a lot of work to do as well. I firmly believe that the number one reason people died April 27 was the siren mentality. The notion that you should hear some magical air raid siren before a tornado strikes. Outdoor sirens have NEVER been effective in reaching people indoors in a home, business, car, school, or church. You might hear them being tested on a bright sunny day, but if you think you are going to hear one during a raging storm in the middle of the night, you simply don't have much hope.

It really didn't hit us until the following year. On January 23, 2012, a pre-dawn tornado (an EF-3) moved through the Birmingham suburbs of Center Point and Clay. It killed a 16-year-old girl, Christina Heichelbech. She was a beautiful, brilliant student at Shades Valley High School, with her entire life in front of her. She was an only child. Her parents survived the tornado, and later that day the grieving father, Darrell, said they "never heard the siren."

I decided that day that a bold message on stopping siren dependency was seriously needed. No telling how many people nationally have died for the same reason. . .waiting on some siren that could never be heard as a tornado approached.

Christina's parents, Darrell and Carol, have been strong advocates for stopping the siren mentality, and I am so thankful for their hearts. We have to move from sirens to a two-tiered approach: having a NOAA Weather Radio in every home and business, and having a good warning app on all smartphones. And, the truth is that all phones should have an audible tornado warning alarm thanks to Wireless Emergency Alerts (WEA). Please don't turn off those WEA alerts; they could save your life.

We have learned that most people can't find their house on a map. And, we use mostly maps during life-threatening weather. Geography literacy is a big problem in this country; most people now just ask their phones about where they want to go, and they get step-by-step directions without the need for looking at maps.

I wish this would change, but it is what it is. We have to get past maps and use a communication technique people can understand when tornadoes are down. This is going to require a lot of thought and help from social scientists.

I did little to reach the Hispanic community in Alabama on April 27. Some of those who were killed didn't understand what we were saying, and what it all meant. It is our charge to protect all human life, and I need to do better. I don't know Spanish, but there are many opportunities with local Spanish radio stations and our various TV sub-channels.

I am in the process of memorizing the names of all 252 people who were killed by the generational tornado outbreak of April 27, 2011. I don't want their memory to just fade away; knowing the names and the stories keeps me focused and energized as we work in making the warning process better and more efficient.

CHAPTER 38
SNOWMAGEDDON

No doubt the great Alabama Ice Storm of 1982 is the worst forecast bust in my long career. Number two on the list came in January 2014. The month started off with fairly pleasant conditions; in fact, we enjoyed a high of 65 degrees on the eleventh of the month. On January 27, the high was a fairly comfortable 53.

But also on January 27, we were forecasting a significant winter storm for the southern half of Alabama, with potential for significant snow from Montgomery south. I wrote the following on the afternoon blog discussion on January 27:

Light snow could break out across Alabama early tomorrow morning. Yes, we do expect snow in places like Birmingham, Tuscaloosa, Anniston, and Gadsden, but generally it should be very light and scattered, and no significant accumulation is expected. Maybe a dusting in a few spots. Travel issues are not expected through North/Central Alabama.

Let me say that I will have a very hard time saying the words "dusting" and "travel issues are not expected" again. The snow around the I-20 corridor (including population centers like Birmingham, Tuscaloosa, and Anniston) was actually only a little more than a dusting, between one and two inches. But the idea of "no travel issues" was a massive bust.

Alabama State Troopers responded to 731 vehicle accidents across the state from January 28 to January 31. There were nine deaths attributed to accidents that occurred due to extremely icy road conditions. Some were stranded on highways for over 15 hours. Most of those people simple abandoned their vehicles and started walking, looking for shelter. Some who ran out of gas on interstates started fires on the side of the road to stay warm.

Students in schools could not go home; they spent multiple nights in those school buildings with their teachers and school staff members. Parents were separated from their children, in some cases for days. Most businesses were shut down, and there was general chaos.

On January 28, 2014, I was headed to Northside Middle School in the north part of Tuscaloosa County for a school program that morning. As I was leaving Birmingham, light snow started to fall, which was part of the forecast. I stopped at the Rest Area along I-59/20 at Brookwood and checked Twitter. Scrolling through the feed, I saw dozens of tweets showing car crashes in Tuscaloosa and other parts of West Alabama, where the snow had been falling for a longer period of time. At that moment, I didn't need to think, I had to react. I knew something was going horribly wrong with the forecast, and I had to get back to the ABC 33/40 studio in Hoover. I called the school to let them know I wasn't coming and headed back. By the time I got off I-459 in Hoover, my car was doing some serious fish tailing. I was almost hit by another guy losing control of his car, and at that point I was just praying I could make it back to the station.

Thankfully, I did make it onto Riverchase Parkway, but after turning off U.S. 31 onto the Parkway I hit total gridlock due to multiple crashes. I sat there for about 15 minutes, and made the decision to get out of the car and walk to work. It was only about one mile, and it seemed like everyone else was out of their vehicles and walking was well.

That was the longest one mile walk in my life. I wished I had a bag to put over my head as I walked past the major employers on Riverchase Parkway; I would not blame the folks at Blue Cross/Blue Shield and Regions if they had pelted me with snowballs or screamed obscenities at me. But during that walk I tried to remain focused; I knew the minute I got into the station I had to go on the air and change everyone's thinking. The natural reaction during something like this is that people need to pick up their children and get home. But, in this case, that was the wrong thing to do.

If people were in a warm place with food, they had to stay put. The kids would be fine; the teachers and lunchroom workers at schools wouldn't be going anywhere either. By getting on the road, people risked being in a serious crash or being stranded for a very long period of time. That was the lesson learned in the January 1982 debacle.

How in the world could one to two inches of snow bring us down into a state of total chaos? The key in this case was the depth of the cold air in the lower levels of the atmosphere. In almost every case, when it snows in Alabama, temperatures are in the 30-35 degree range. Below those levels, the air is usually too dry for any wintry precipitation.

But, on January 28, 2014, the temperature was hovering between 18 and 22 degrees as the snow was falling that morning. Lesson learned here? The ice accretion process on roads is radically different when the air is that cold. As the snow initially came down, there was some melting, and within minutes the water turned to ice basically causing a flash freeze on roads. And, in my long tenure here, I had no experience with this. The one-to-two-inch snow had the impact of a major ice storm in terms of travel.

And, when everyone realized the idea of "no travel issues" was dead wrong, everyone left at the same time (mid-morning) trying to get home. The combination of ice covered roads and extreme traffic volume went on to paralyze the region for days.

Needless to say, there were all kinds of vitriol directed at me in the days following "Snowmageddon," and it was deserved. People were tired and hungry, in strange places trying to sleep away from their families and children, and needed to vent.

I encouraged people not to vent at school officials or their bosses. They made decisions on weather forecasts, and what they got was bad information. I was the one to blame.

This is an example of what I saw in the email inbox on January 29:

> *Looks like you got it wrong yesterday with your prediction of a light dusting and no accumulation. How can you guys be so badly off as hundreds still sit in their schools and hundreds remain in their cars on highways and no telling how many have had to leave their cars stranded and knock on strangers' doors for shelter while others have paid the ultimate price trying to drive? How can you be so wrong? Has everything with your career over the past years gone to your head? You are still expected to be vigilant and not complacent. What a shame as I think of the people still out there and the ones who are dead. . . .*

I won't share the name who wrote this, but it was signed. The criticism is valid, and I took it to heart. I appreciate her taking the time to write, and I mean that. For weather professionals, we have to understand the difference between constructive criticism and trolls, haters, and know-it-alls.

Another thought: I am not sure we are actually qualified to talk about travel conditions anyway. We are trained in atmospheric science, not road engineering. It goes back to "tell them what you know, and don't tell them what you don't know."

Winter weather forecasting is always a challenge; this is where we can make our greatest improvement in coming years.

CHAPTER 39
CLIMATE CHANGE

I hold by my long-standing policy not to comment on politics, or politicians. Quite frankly, I can't. I am technically in a news department at a television station, which prohibits it. Truthfully, I know absolutely nothing about journalism; I am employed as a meteorologist. But, most of us in television weather are working under the news umbrella. We are much like place kickers on a football team.

If you want thoughts from others on politics, just open up your Facebook feed, or check Twitter. Seems like I might be the only person on the planet with no comment on the subject. Long-time readers know I actually despise politics; I have seen it divide our nation and put so many people in a constant rage. Will there ever be a time to focus on the things that bring us together, instead of the things that tear us apart? And, anyway, people follow me for weather information, not advice on voting.

The only comment I have is that I am thankful for the votes I received in the 2017 U.S. Senate race in 14 Alabama counties. The fact that people were writing in a meteorologist is a sign of the odd times we are in.

Tweets from U.S. President Donald Trump during his tenure have stirred the pot on the climate issue, much like this one posted on December 27, 2017, during a cold snap over the eastern half of the nation:

In the East, it could be the COLDEST New Year's Eve on record. Perhaps we could use a little bit of that good old Global Warming that our Country, but not other countries, was going to pay TRILLIONS OF DOLLARS to protect against. Bundle up!

Even a fifth grader knows a cold snap doesn't disprove anthropogenic climate change. Some reaction from the science/climate community. . .

My friend Dr. Marshall Shepherd from the University of Georgia: *"On science literacy, we are in a sad state of affairs. . . .it is truly almost embarrassing what some people tweet or post with a straight face . . . . Just wow"*

Another colleague, Alan Gerard, with the National Severe Storms Laboratory, made a very valid point. . . *"I will say that it would probably help climate change education if we as professionals focused our message on climate level events - and not on looking for and trumpeting a 'climate change signal' on every extreme weather event."*

I would suggest that climate activists have opened the door to comments like "what happened to global warming?" when it turns cold. Seems like every time we have a tornado, hurricane, flood, wildfire, heat wave, or drought, there are those that rush to blame it on climate change or suggest the event was magnified by it. Have we totally forgotten the difference between climate and weather? Or, does weather simply not exist anymore?

Bill Nye (who has no background in meteorology) is by far the worst offender. After a series of tornadoes touched down in May 2016, he frantically put this out on Twitter: *"More severe weather. More suffering. More expense. Let's all take climate change seriously."*

Climate attribution studies take months and in most cases, years of work. Getting on the "tweeter" and proclaiming nonsense like this concerning weather events does your cause no good.

Is there any way to stop the rhetoric and discuss climate without the vitriol? Even within the science community? I do believe there is great common ground. Can we agree on the following things?

*The climate is changing. Always has and always will. I have never heard of a "climate change denier". What some dispute and deny is that man-made greenhouse gases are the primary driver/control knob of climate change.

*CO_2 is a greenhouse gas. Actually, the life blood of the planet. But, too much of a good thing can be bad. Very bad.

*We need to take care of the planet. It is our home.

*Human life is precious.

The debate involves the role of man in climate change. And, we can have healthy debate and conversation. The time has come to treat those that disagree with you with propriety and respect. That is my definition of *tolerance*.

Most know I am a skeptic of some AGW (Anthropogenic Global Warming) claims. In my opinion, skepticism is one of the most valuable tools in science. Continual questioning of ideas and results is a means of overturning some long-held assumptions (that turn out to be false) and uncovering new ideas.

Is there some anthropogenic climate forcing? Yes, there has to be. But, what in the world happened to natural variability? Natural climate drivers include changes in the sun's energy output, regular changes in Earth's orbital cycle, and large volcanic eruptions that put light-reflecting particles into the upper atmosphere. I am afraid so many heavily involved in the climate debate deny this truth. What happens when the AMO (Atlantic Multidecadal Oscillation) flips to a cold phase? The AMO is a coherent mode of natural variability occurring in the North Atlantic Ocean with an estimated period of 60-80 years.

I actually support the same end game as the climate change zealots. If somehow people can cut out the hate, anger, and rage, and just take a deep breath, you might be surprised to see how much we have in common.

I am not a fan of dumping increasing amounts of CO_2 into the atmosphere. Fossil fuels have given us a wonderful lifestyle with affordable energy, but we need to look at alternative sources now.

Do I like "big oil"? No. I will be the first in line to get an electric vehicle as soon as it can get me to a long distance school visit without the need for a charge during the journey (and I don't have to take out a mortgage to get one). I believe one day we'll look back at the internal combustion engines we use now and get a good laugh.

But, there has to be a slow phase-in process during the move away from fossil fuel. Cut off affordable energy, and there will be genuine human suffering. There is a solution here if we can get away from the extremist positions (on both sides) and meet in the middle.

As I have done many times, I encourage people to think for themselves. Ask good questions, and don't mock those who have a different opinion. Don't let politicians (those on the right, and those on the left) and entertainers be your source of climate change information.

I encourage you to get out of your echo chamber and listen to those who might have a different opinion. I am committed to it, and I hope you are too. Maybe a crazy Trump tweet can get a good conversation started.

CHAPTER 40
NO SLEEP, BUT HAVING FUN

Often people ask me how much sleep I get. My standard answer is "I haven't slept much since 1973." And, trust me, that is a true statement. It was in 1973 when I started working late nights on WTBC radio and came in after a short nap to sign on the sister FM station while I was in high school in Tuscaloosa.

My job has morphed into a career that allows little time for sleep. My alarm goes off sometime between 3:45 and 4:45 a.m. weekday mornings. Most mornings, 4:45. But, on days with a long road trip for a school visit, it will be closer to 3:45 to allow time to get the morning production done.

In the morning, I work a shift in my home office, yes, complete with a green chroma-key wall. I do forecasting and analysis, write a blog discussion, produce the *Weather Xtreme* video, do a segment on ABC 33/40's *Good Morning Alabama*, and do weather on over a dozen radio stations. Many mornings I am live on the nationally syndicated "Rick and Bubba" show. Those guys do video as well. For years it simply didn't matter what I was wearing while I was getting all this work done, but now with the segments on ABC 33/40 and Rick and Bubba, I at least have a decent looking shirt on. Am I wearing pants, though? That is the big question--for me to know and you to find out.

After the morning shift, I am off to a school visit or speaking engagement. I am in one or two schools just about every day during the school year. And, in summer, there are so many programs for kids that there isn't much of a slowdown. On occasion, I will speak to a service club or senior adult group. My calendar is always jammed, often 8-12 months in advance.

I am also Chairman of the Board at a large hospital in Birmingham, Grandview Medical Center. In addition to the monthly board meetings, I do my best to walk the floors of the hospital once a week to talk with our employees, our patients, and their families. You won't know what happens in a large complex like that unless you spend some time there.

Doing the school visits is win-win-win. I love teaching science, especially to elementary school kids. The kids get excited about meteorology, and I learn the state of Alabama while driving. Some ask me how I know the state so well; after 40 years of driving to schools, it just happens.

One thing I have done is block out a one hour window Monday, Wednesday, and Friday during the middle of the day to work out and get some exercise. You can find me at Godspeed Elite Sports Academy, right across the street from ABC 33/40 in Riverchase. This is a big commitment; it means the long road trips can only happen Tuesdays and Thursdays; I schedule all the short distance schools before the workouts. Some days I do a local school before AND after the workout.

In 2015 I was overweight, and really struggling with fatigue by the time the late news hit the air. I started the workout schedule to change that. It was very hard at first, and I threw up after the third session. But, with time, I started seeing the benefits with weight loss and higher energy levels.

I am very thankful for Lance Rhodes, Blake Prime, and Sean Thompson at Godspeed for making me a better person, both physically and spiritually.

I come into the office (better known as the *WeatherBrains* corporate headquarters, nothing more than a closet) about 2:00 p.m. I take another look at more data, write another blog discussion, and do another *Weather Xtreme* video. Then, I go on ABC 33/40 at 4:00 and pretty much stay in the TV studio through the end of the long evening news block at 6:30.

I should mention that on most Fridays I have a family with me in the studio; many high school kids are interested in majoring in meteorology, and I let them come visit for a firsthand look at what we do.

On Monday nights at 6:30 I run over to Ragtime Cafe, by the station, for a quick meal with my Sunday night tennis pals and then get back to the closet at 8:00 to prep our weekly podcast, *WeatherBrains,* which has been in production since 2006. This is the longest running weather podcast in the universe, and one of my creative outlets during the week. The show usually runs from 8:30 until 10:00 p.m. CT; we are live on YouTube even though most people simply listen to the podcast version. We have had just about every big shot in the weather enterprise on the show over the years and I work on the show with a wonderful group of professionals from around the country.

Tuesday through Friday nights, I usually run home to see Karen and spend some time with her during the break between the 6:00 and 10:00 newscasts. And, yes, take a nap.

I do weather on *ABC 33/40 News at 10:00* and usually leave the station about 11:00. When I get home, I have to prep graphics for the morning segment on *Good Morning Alabama* on ABC 33/40 and respond to questions and comments across the various digital platforms. Most nights I fall asleep about 1:00 a.m.

And, in a few hours, the alarm is sounding again and a new day begins.

Of course, all throughout the long days, I deal with the monster known as social media. I have no idea why so many people follow me, but as of the time I am writing this book, here is my follower count:

Facebook 554,000
Twitter 412,000
Instagram 141,000

I won't even count Snapchat, YouTube, or others, but as you can see my combined follower count is over one million. With these large numbers, I get an overwhelming number of private messages, questions, and comments that require an answer. It is very much like the famous chocolate factory scene in "I Love Lucy"; they simply come in sometimes faster than I can answer or respond.

Let me say that I am honored when anyone comes to me with a weather question. Of all the weather people in the world, they chose me. I am honored, and I will do my best to answer. But, it takes time, and you have to learn to multitask to get it done.

And, of course, on all these platforms I need to be pushing interesting, relevant, and compelling content. I work hard to make that happen.

I totally understand getting 3-4 hours of sleep a night isn't healthy. But, to be successful in this business today, you must work long hours and work on short naps. Thankfully I do get to sleep a bit longer on weekends when the weather is quiet.

CHAPTER 41
THE FUTURE

I hear it often. The era of the television meteorologists is over. Smartphone apps have replaced them. Who needs James Spann? I have a cool phone app!

I will say our business has been disrupted, and things will never be the same. The same business model that has supported me and my family for 40 years will end sooner than later. But, at the same time, the need for what we do will never go away.

When a tornado is bearing down on your neighborhood, there is a very high probability you aren't going to be looking at the crap app on your phone with a high, low, probability of precipitation, and a little cartoon drawing of a thunderstorm. You are going to seek out a live video stream of a professional, experienced meteorologist with strong communication skill and true knowledge of the science--someone who understands the people and the geography of the region.

Even on routine weather days, that phone app tells you nothing about the uncertainty, coverage, placement, and magnitude of the type of event that is being forecast. Yes, no doubt people get weather from their phones first, but we can, and should be the ones who provide a higher quality of weather information than is on that phone.

Will local television news survive? Most likely not in its current form. Ratings are still strong in the morning and evening news blocks; the main struggle is late news (10:00 in my market). Many nights ABC programming delivers ratings in the 1-3 range; 20 years ago we often had shows with a 15-20 point rating. So many are "cutting the cord" and watching streaming programming on their Roku or Apple TV from Netflix, Amazon, or other sources. And, most people already know the news of the day; they are bombarded with news all day with the 24-hour cable networks and their phones. They don't see a need to watch the local 10:00 news unless there is some really compelling content or if we are expecting a big weather event the following day.

For now, in the weather segments of these newscasts we simply have to give context and information people can't get on their phones. We have to be interesting and energetic. Consultants come in and tell you if you say the words *track* or *tracking* every other sentence, then people will flock to the newscasts. Or, make a bunch of fancy graphics and folks will turn off Netflix and watch the late news.

I believe instead of spending four hours a day making fancy graphics, we need to be in schools and out among our viewers, establishing a personal relationship with them. Television meteorologists need to weave themselves into the fabric of the local culture and become part of the family. This means not spending all day in a TV studio, but spending time on the road and with the people. This beats fancy graphics every time.

And, saying *track* or *tracking* every other sentence (like the consultants suggest) gives people the impression you have some kind of mental disorder. Long time *WeatherBrains* listeners know our disdain for this one.

At least our platform is not going away. For my friends in the newspaper business, print is dead. For those of us in television, people will have multiple devices to consume video programming. We simply have to provide compelling, relevant content. We can't do the same thing we did in 1975, 1995, or even 2015. The people watching local television news are old and getting older. At some point we have to learn to attract a younger audience. I don't think we do that by dumbing down anything; we simply have to get to know them, learn what they want, and make it happen.

Understand I do weather. I don't have time to worry about television business models; I simply have to focus on providing good, quality, consistent content daily across multiple platforms and developing a large, loyal, and engaged audience. Good things will follow and I will survive all the changes ahead.

When I hire people for my weather office, I look for these qualities…

*People with a passion for weather who are willing to work hard. After 40 years in this business, I still can't wait to come to work every day. And, I will work harder than anyone else to accomplish a task. Are you like that? Then I want you in my operation. Nobody wants a negative Nellie or someone who is lazy. If that is you, then you don't have much hope.

*Integrity. Doing the right thing even when nobody's looking. In fact, what you do when nobody is looking pretty much defines who you really are. We all make mistakes; in fact, my middle name should be *mistake*. But you learn from them and never go down that road again.

*A servant's heart. It's not about you. If you are genuinely willing to put the needs of others before your own, you will be successful. I didn't figure this out until I was in my late 30s. The job of a meteorologist is that of a servant, and you need to get that from the beginning.

For young people just entering our business, I am bullish on their future. They will carve out a new model and do things we could not dream of doing during my career.

I am also very positive on the advancements ahead in the weather enterprise. This feeling is based on the quality of young people entering the science and the intense, never ending quest for knowledge and solutions. No doubt our understanding of synoptic and mesoscale meteorological processes will increase exponentially in coming years thanks to better and higher resolution remote sensing and better computing power providing higher quality Numerical Weather Prediction (NWP) output and deep research projects now underway that will solve some, but not all, of the mysteries of the atmosphere.

My focus for the last years of my career is improving the severe weather warning process. Way too many people have died on my watch over the past 40 years. We have learned we have to take an interdisciplinary approach to severe weather warnings. Weaving social science into physical science is critical, as well as the entire weather enterprise communicating a simple, unified message during life-threatening weather.

CHAPTER 42
WHAT WE LEAVE BEHIND

At my age, I often think about my legacy. History will be the judge, but I don't want to be remembered for my length of service, awards won, ratings success, or the number of Twitter followers. I am hoping some will recall my determination to guide people and keep them safe during dangerous weather and will remember me for putting something back into the community that has been so good to me over the years.

Vacation Bible School

The only two things that really matter in life are your relationship with God and how you treat other people. They are deeply entwined. One minute you are in diapers, and in a flash, you are nearing your final breath on this Earth. Our days here are long, but the years are short. Time does seem to accelerate as you get older.

I often have a vision of two lines of people; one is like the line at Space Mountain at Disney World--so long you have no idea where it begins or ends. These are the people I encountered in my daily journey with serious needs and I chose to walk right past them, never lifting a finger to help. The other line is very short, and those are the ones I did choose to assist. My goal in life now is to try to make those two lines equal. It will never happen, but I can try.

Despite some hardships and the daily pressure of television weather, I have lived a blessed life. Instead of chasing good jobs, they have literally chased me. A quick, crude calculation shows that I have done the weather segment in a little over 50,000 newscasts since the summer of 1978. I can say with confidence that I have enjoyed every one of them. I get paid to communicate practical information about the science I love.

And, while I have been in the same local TV market most of my career, the Internet era expanded my reach, and I love having followers nationally and globally. *WeatherBrains* has a large and loyal following; I never dreamed that would happen when a group of weather weenies started the show in 2006. I am honored when people choose to watch me on television, to read one of my blog discussions, to watch a *Weather Xtreme* video, or to listen to *WeatherBrains*. You are part of my extended family and the words of encouragement I receive sure make dealing with trolls easier.

Let me end with a salute to those who came before me, paving the way for my generation of broadcast meteorologists. People like Harold Taft from Dallas, Roy Leep of Tampa, Dick Goddard of Cleveland, Gary England of Oklahoma City, Bob Ryan of Washington, and Nash Roberts of New Orleans. You might recall Nash was the man I heard on WWL in August of 1969 as Camille approached the Gulf Coast.

In 2013, I was so honored to receive the "Award for Broadcast Meteorology" from the American Meteorological Society. It is pretty much the highest honor for a person in broadcast meteorology. And, before the awards banquet, I got to spend a little time with Bob

Ryan, who was the winner the previous year. I really enjoyed watching Bob when he was the meteorologist on the *Today Show* on NBC, before transferring to WRC, the local NBC station in Washington.

Karen took this photo; this was when I accepted the American Meteorological Society Award for Broadcast Meteorology in January 2013. It was presented by Louis Uccellini, the director of the National Weather Service.

I am very thankful for the influence these broadcast meteorologists had on me, and I can only hope to have a small role in shaping the future career of young people with a true fascination with weather. On Fridays, I have families visit me at ABC 33/40; typically, they have one child that loves weather and has an interest in getting into meteorology. That child might be six years old or perhaps a junior in high school. That particular child gets the "executive tour," watches the 5:00 news in the studio, and gets a shot at working the big green wall at 5:30. I know for a fact that this treatment has launched a number of careers.

If a low income, fatherless child from rural South Alabama can live the dream, you can too. No doubt your path will be different, but do everything important in your life with passion, integrity, and a servant's heart, and you will be successful as well.